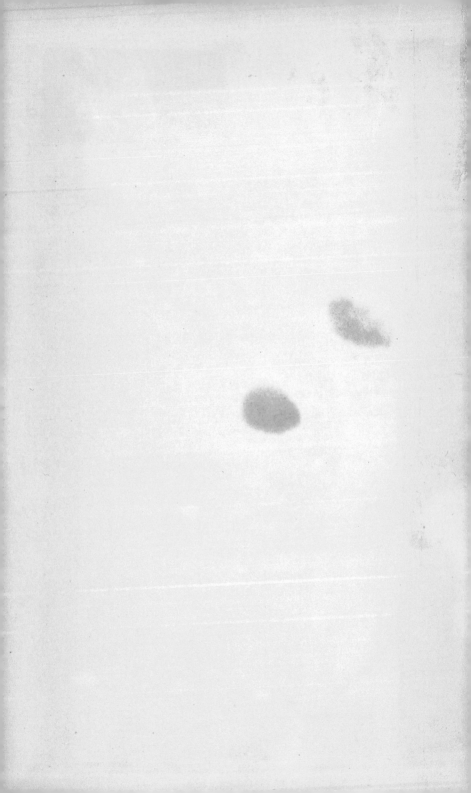

IRISH AGRICULTURE
IN TRANSITION

DOVEA HOUSE

IRISH AGRICULTURE IN TRANSITION

BY

JOSEPH JOHNSTON, M.A. (Dubl., Oxon.)

Senior Fellow of Trinity College, Dublin ;
Professor of Applied Economics ; President
of the Social and Statistical Inquiry
Society of Ireland

With an Introduction by

PROFESSOR T. A. SMIDDY

DUBLIN: HODGES, FIGGIS AND CO., LTD
6 DAWSON STREET
OXFORD: BASIL BLACKWELL
1951

Printed by THE DUBLIN UNIVERSITY PRESS, LTD.

DEDICATED TO THE MEMORY OF
SIR HORACE PLUNKETT

AUTHOR'S PREFACE

"Irish Agriculture in Transition" is an effort to assess the present position and prospective development of the agricultural economy of the Republic of Ireland. The first part of the book is an interpretation of the historical and statistical background from the point of view of the post-war era.

The influence of the Land War and its settlement is noted as a persistent factor in Irish rural psychology. The two great institutions founded by Sir Horace Plunkett—the I.A.O.S. and the Department of Agriculture—are placed in historical perspective.

The long-term tendency to specialise in producing live stock and live stock products, and export the surplus to Great Britain, is explained historically and illustrated statistically. The continuing effect of the so-called Economic War of 1932–1938, and of the second World War, in interrupting and perverting this tendency is emphasised. An analysis of the capital assets of Irish agriculture, as in 1939, helps to explain the low output per person and per acre that characterises our agriculture.

The author was concerned as a member of the Post-Emergency Committee on Agricultural Policy of 1942–1945 in drafting the Majority Report on Agricultural Policy which has since, in the main, become the accepted policy of two successive governments. When it became possible after the restrictions of the "Emergency" period, he renewed his personal contacts with a few of our agricultural regions. This enabled him to observe and record some of the dynamic factors which are now shaping the future of rural Ireland. The second part of the book "Contemporary Influences and Trends" contains a number of such "field studies" which serve to illustrate the more general descriptive matter of the first part. As "sample" investigations they also indicate the desirability of a comprehensive survey of agricultural conditions and possibilities in the country as a whole.

In a final chapter on the "Local integration of Agricultural Effort" it is pointed out that modern techniques and the growing need for expensive capital equipment have outmoded the typical 30-acre farm as an economic unit. Suggestions are made for a closer integration of agricultural effort which would involve the organised application of co-operative principles to production on individually owned farms as well as to the processing and sale of agricultural products and the purchase of raw materials. If these suggestions were adopted a new rural civilisation would evolve in which Better Living would be more readily realised as well as Better Farming and Better Business.

Ever since he travelled round the world as an Albert Kahn Fellow in 1914–1915 the present writer has been interested in agriculture, and not only in Irish Agriculture. He used to accompany one of the organisers of the I.A.O.S. in subsequent years and "say a few words" at the end of each meeting. So long as his interest in Irish Agriculture was merely academic, he was listened to politely, but with obvious lack of interest. Later on he acquired a country residence and took up small scale farming as a hobby. At a critical point, when he was expanding the scale of his operations, he suffered a "head on" collision with the outbreak of the Economic War. That caused him to "think furiously," and, for the first time, to realise where the shoe pinched from the point of view of those depending on agriculture for a livelihood. At the same time his Platonic instinct to seek for the One in the Many led him to consult authoritative works and statistical records with new understanding. Ever since that time his views on Irish agricultural problems have been listened to by Irish farmers with a degree of respect which, formerly, they did not receive or perhaps deserve. But he would like to say with all possible emphasis that in a real sense he, in turn, has learnt much from Irish farmers, and this book owes much to their teaching. The literary sources of information, which have also been used or referred to, are listed in the bibliography.

Like Topsy this book "just growed." It began as an article in the *Economic Journal,* on "Price Ratios in Recent Irish Agricultural Experience," which appeared in December 1937. Thanks are due to the Editors for permission to reprint it in a more up to date form. It continued in the form of various papers read from time to time to the Statistical and Social Inquiry Society of Ireland. Their inclusion in the text appears to be justified, since lapse of time has added to their historical interest without detracting from their relevance to our present problems. The author is indebted to the Council of the Society for permission to republish them in a revised and modified form. He acknowledges similar obligations to the Editors of the *Manchester Guardian,* the *Irish (Times) Review and Annual,* the *Irish Independent,* and the *Irish Farmers' Journal.*

He is also indebted to Professor Duncan, F.T.C.D., and to Professor George O'Brien, for much encouragement and help. Dr. Moody, F.T.C.D., made valuable suggestions for the arrangement of the subject matter which he was very glad to adopt. Dr. George Adams, who is an old and valued friend of every good Irish cause, drew his attention to a serious omission in the semi-final draft, which, fortunately, was easy to remedy. Dr. Adams was also most helpful in other ways—needless to say, none of the persons referred to here, or in the text, is in any way responsible for any personal views expressed in the following pages.

Finally, he is indebted to the Board of Trinity College for a generous grant from the Madden Fund which has greatly facilitated publication.

JOSEPH JOHNSTON.

TRINITY COLLEGE,
DUBLIN,
   July, 1951.

CONTENTS

PART I—HISTORICAL AND STATISTICAL.

CHAPTER   PAGE

    I. The Legacy of the Land War - - 3

   II. Agencies of Agricultural Policy - - 20

  III. Agricultural Policy after 1922 - - 30

  IV. Raw Materials for Irish Animal Husbandry 35

   V. Speeding the Plough - - - 49

  VI. Feed Costs and Animal Product Prices - 56

 VII. Éire Bounties and British Penal Duties - 72

VIII. The Capital Assets of Irish Agriculture in
        1939 - - - - - 87

PART II.—CONTEMPORARY INFLUENCES AND TRENDS.

    XI. The New Attitude to Grass - - - 105

     X. Signs of Change in Livestock Policy - 109

    XI. Developments in Poultry Policy - - 112

   XII. The Progress of Mechanisation - - 116

 XIII. Women on the Farm - - - - 120

 XIV. Three Co-operatively Owned Farms - - 125

  XV. A "Workhouse" that is a Workhouse - 135

 XVI. Dovea Co-Operative Farm - - - 139

XVII. Mitchelstown Co-Operative Farm - - 147

XVIII. The Outlook in 1950 and 1951 - - 154

 XIX. The Local Integration of Agricultural Effort 163

ILLUSTRATIONS

Dovea House - - - - *frontispiece*

Aerial view of Gurteen Agricultural College *facing* p. 122

Hay Sheds and Grass Silos at Dovea House
Co-Operative Creamery Farm - - ,, p. 138

DIAGRAMS

	PAGE
I. Application of Phosphate on Irish Land -	54
II. Ratio of Feed Cost to price of Beef Cattle -	64
III. Ratio of Feed Cost to price of Eggs - -	67
IV. Ratio of Feed Cost to price of Pigs - -	71
V. U.K. Tax and Eire Bounties on certain exports between 1933 and 1937 - - -	87

Map—Agricultural Co-Operative Societies *facing* p. 178

INTRODUCTION

PROFESSOR JOHNSTON analyses the structure of our agricultural economy and shows the historical and economic factors which have given rise to it. He indicates the lines along which its development should take place and which should be as far as possible in accordance with its natural and traditional conditions.

He sets forth with lucidity the extent to which the structure of our agriculture is determined by the British market which he illustrates by the effects of the Economic dispute with Great Britain.

His chapter on bounties and subsidies is a valuable contribution to the subject of agricultural economics. He shows how much they distort the natural development of our farming resources.

His chapters on co-operative creameries are informative and interesting and show what the capabilities of co-operation are under the limited conditions in which it operates. Apart from co-operative creameries he indicates how little co-operative spirit exists among the farming community.

His analysis of the economy of large-scale and small-scale farming is informative. While he deprecates generally the breaking-up of large-scale efficiently worked holdings into small ones, yet, he asserts that in Ireland a combination of large-scale, medium size and small-scale holdings of economic size, fits in with our natural agronomy. He shows that farmyard industry—pigs and poultry—is essential to give the small farmer an adequate standard of living. Such small-scale farming is dependent on imported feeding stuffs or on supplies from the large-scale farmers who can till profitably.

Professor Johnston combines in his treatment of the subject the academic and the realistic approach to the subject. He has studied, over many years, the subject of agriculture and has written and lectured on many of its problems. The Statistical and Social Inquiry Society of Ireland, of which he is now President, has on many occasions benefited by the many papers he read. He is familiar with the circumstances of the "small-size" farmer and has for many years farmed successfully a small-scale economic holding. Further, he has gained first-hand information from his many contacts with farmers of all sizes of farms. Hence, his approach to the subject is thoroughly practical. He was an active member of the Committee on Post-Emergency Agricultural Policy, where the various problems of agriculture were under review. He was responsible for drafting a large part of the majority Report, which was in large measure adopted by the last and the present Government.

In his opinion progress among farmers along scientific lines and the adoption of more intensive rather than extensive farming, as well as the investment of his savings in such development, will be in a large measure fostered by more education among the younger men and women for which achievement the Young Farmers' Clubs and "Muintirs" give hope.

The book is a valuable contribution to the agricultural Economics of Ireland, while its simple and lucid style will make its reading attractive for the ordinary reader.

T. A. SMIDDY

(*Chairman of the Committee of Inquiry on Post-Emergency Agricultural Policy*).

DUBLIN,
January, 1951.

PART I

HISTORICAL AND STATISTICAL

CHAPTER I

The Legacy of the Land War

STUDENTS of Irish Agriculture at the beginning of the present century were obsessed by the phenomena of Irish land tenure. The "Irish question" was coming to be considered a "Land question" and the land question was a question of the very unsatisfactory relations between landlords and tenants. A classical work on this subject called "Modern Ireland and her Agrarian Problem" was written by a very competent German observer, Dr. Moritz J. Bonn, and appeared in an English translation in 1906.

By that date the opinion had crystallised, both in Ireland and Great Britain, that the ideal solution of the secular problem was the transformation of occupying tenants into peasant proprietors by a process of state financed land purchase.

The Wyndham Act of 1903 was the first major step in this direction, and the process was completed by the Land Acts of 1923 and 1925. By that date a self-governing Irish Free State had been established in the twenty-six southern counties and Northern Ireland had been provided with a subordinate Parliament as part of the "United Kingdom."

If the "magic of ownership" was enough to turn sand into gold, the subsequent history of Irish Agriculture, north and south, should have been a record of continuous progress. That it has been nothing of the kind will be very clear from later pages of this book. The occurrence of two World Wars, a World Slump, and an Economic War (which only affected the southern area) do not fully account for failure to make continuous progress. The legacy of the past also exercised a retarding influence, and this was true, not only with reference to the facts of social and economic structure, but also with reference to what may be called the ideological tradition. For centuries Irish farmers had been subjected to a State-imposed oppression which only the State could remove and remedy. The idea that "the Government" is the source of all possible benefactions became an integral part of the subconscious (rural) Irish mind. It is true that the pioneers of the Agricultural Co-operative movement—Sir Horace Plunkett and his associates—preached a doctrine of self-help through mutual help, not without a certain measure of success. But the movement never really captured the soul of Ireland, and its material success in recent decades seems to have coincided with a phase of arrested development in the more important spiritual sphere. There have been encouraging recent signs of stirring among the dry bones, and the vigorous activities of the Young Farmers' Clubs and Muintir-na-Tire give reason to hope that we stand on the threshold of a new and more fruitful era.

One object of this book is to make clear by an objective analysis those "missing components" in former policies which help to account for their disappointing results, those demoralising bye-products of former policies which still exercise a baleful influence, and those objective facts of our present economic circumstances which must be clearly realised if appropriate policies of national, regional and local initiative are to make possible the most desirable results.

During the first seven decades of the nineteenth century British land legislation for Ireland aimed at strengthening the social and legal position of the Irish landlords, a thousand of whom were the legal owners of more than half the country. Ever since the end of the seventeenth century the individual members of this class had possessed, in their various local areas, a degree of social power, for good or evil, which was practically absolute.

Arthur Young wrote: "The power and influence of a resident landlord is so great in Ireland, that whatever system he adopts, be it well or ill imagined, he is much more able to introduce or accomplish it than Englishmen can well have an idea of." (*A Tour in Ireland*, ed. Hutton, vol. II, p. 105.)

Most Irish landlords were demoralised by the high and increasing rents which it was possible to levy during the Napoleonic era of rising prices. For decades they lived beyond their means, and with a few honourable exceptions did nothing for the development of their estates and provided none of those long term services for their tenants, which were regularly supplied in England and Scotland, and were in fact the economic justification for agricultural rents. As Dr. Bonn puts it, "the landlord's house at the best was only an important centre of consumption, and very rarely the central point of a great scheme of management embracing the entire property" (p. 64). Dr. Bonn goes on to add that this class had to suffer for the sins of its useless members, and that it fulfilled its political and economic duties ill enough and produced neither a policy nor a leader during the great agrarian revolution which brought about its fall.

In the year 1870 there were 682,237 farms in Ireland, of which 135,392 were leaseholds and 526,628 belonged to the class of yearly tenancies. A yearly tenancy was terminable at six months' notice without compensation. Only in the case of about twenty estates were the buildings and standing farm equipment provided by the landlords. Such properties were known as English managed estates. In all other cases the tenant had to supply the fixed capital as well as every other form of capital required on his farm. The termination of the tenancy thus enabled the landlord to confiscate the capital invested by the tenant. Between 1849 and 1880 nearly 70,000 families were evicted and dispossessed. The alternative to eviction was willingness and ability to pay a higher rent, and this in fact enabled the landlord to confiscate by another method the capital as well as the industry of an industrious tenant. Between 1850 and 1870, when prices were rising, there was a marked increase of rents.

The real crisis arose when prices began the downward movement in the 70's, which continued until 1896. Meanwhile the political climate in England had changed. John Bright was enthusiastically in favour of creating an Irish peasant proprietary. A foretaste of that eventual solution was provided as a corollary to the Irish Church Disestablishment Act of 1869. The tenants on glebe lands were facilitated in becoming proprietors of their holdings, and most of them did so. However, the Land Acts, passed between 1870 and 1896, were in the main efforts to make landlord-tenant relations more equitable, without abolishing the landlord system as a whole. The Land Act of 1870 legalised an already existing "Ulster Custom" under which.

in that province, a tenant could remain in undisturbed possession so long as he paid his rent, and could sell his interest in his holding at its market value to a new tenant whom the landlord could not, unreasonably, refuse to accept. The Act provided that a tenant in any part of Ireland, who was being arbitrarily evicted, should receive compensation for disturbance and that a tenant on leaving was entitled to compensation for any improvements which he had carried out. For various reasons the Act was a failure. The prices of the more important Irish products tended upwards until 1878 and rents maintained a sympathetic upward surge.

In the year 1878 there began a series of bad harvests, accompanied by a fall of prices which continued for nearly twenty years. The Act of 1870 afforded no protection to a tenant who could not pay his rent. Rents were not readily adjusted downwards by landlords who, as a class, were living in a chronic state of indebtedness and bankruptcy. About the same time John Devoy, Michael Davitt and Charles Stewart Parnell found it convenient to amalgamate the agrarian question with the national movement for political independence. Hence the demand for "the three F's" which was sponsored by the Land League founded by Michael Davitt in 1878. Dr. Bonn rather cynically points out (p. 78) that agrarian reform for a large number of Irish politicians was not an ultimate aim, but a means of keeping alive the claims of national independence.

The years 1878 to 1881 were years of increasing evictions, political turmoil, agrarian crime, and governmental coercion. They culminated in the inevitable surrender to violence of what had been refused to argument, and the famous Land Act of 1881 was passed.

That Act brought into existence the Irish Land Commission, and this was its most permanent if not its most important achievement. For the Irish Land Commission still maintains a continuous organic existence, and in "Eire" at any rate has been perverted to objects which were certainly not contemplated at the time of its foundation. Established in 1881 to provide security of tenure for Irish farmers it became, in the 1930's, a major source of insecurity to many Irish farmers, and both its functions and policies were severely criticised in the Majority Report of the Banking Commission of 1934–1937 (par. 502 ff.).

The Land Act of 1881 abolished freedom of contract in the determination of rents, and provided the machinery for implementing the new principle of the judicial determination of a "fair rent." Henceforth a tenant could only be evicted for non-payment of his rent thus fixed. Thus two of the three F's were secured—fair rent and fixity of tenure. The Act also extended the Ulster Tenant Right system throughout Ireland, and this involved recognition of the third F, freedom of sale.

The Land Act of 1881 carried the principle of dual ownership to its ultimate consequences. It was not yet available to all tenants, but by an Act passed in 1887 leaseholders were admitted to the benefit of it, and this added 150,000 to the number of its beneficiaries.

The dual ownership of Irish land was increasingly felt to be unsatisfactory as a permanent solution. Under it the landlord was a mere rent receiver, and his power for good was destroyed equally with his power for evil. So long as the rent was paid he could not get rid of an unsatisfactory tenant, however much it might be in the public interest that a bad tenant, who was wasting the land, should be replaced by a good one.

The landlord had now no interest in investing capital, by way of long term improvements, in land occupied by his tenants, for he could not count on any return at all, even if he was in a position to make the investment. The tenant, for his part, however much he might expect to gain by "better farming" was reluctant to increase the output from his farm for fear the landlord might get a share of the increase at the next fifteen yearly judicial revision of the rents.

Thus "the baby was thrown out with the bath water," and the system established in 1881, though free from the major evils of the previous system, continued to penalise the social virtues and discourage enterprise.

Ever since the year 1866 John Bright had advocated the establishment of a peasant proprietary in Ireland as the final solution of the land question. In conformity with these ideas the tenants on glebe lands were offered the opportunity of buying out their holdings, the State advancing three-quarters of the purchase money. Actually 6,957 tenants took advantage of this provision of the Church Disestablishment Act of 1869. At Bright's instigation clauses were inserted in the Act of 1870 by which two-thirds of the purchase money could be advanced to a purchasing tenant, and a similar provision in the Act of 1881 authorised the advance of three-quarters. These provisions produced practically no result, chiefly because the tenants were seldom in a position to find a third or a quarter of the purchase money.

The Ashbourne Act of 1885, which was followed by similar Acts in 1891 and 1896, introduced a different principle. Under these Acts the whole of the purchase price was advanced by the State in the form of cash or stock. The tenant became liable, under the terms of the 1885 Act, to an annuity of 4 per cent for a period of forty-nine years. Of the 4 per cent 3 per cent represented interest and 1 per cent sinking fund. All the subsequent Acts embodied the same principle, though there were minor variations of detail.

The principal result of this change was that, under no circumstances, would a purchasing tenant have to pay more, by way of terminable annuity, than he was already liable for as a perpetual rent. As Dr. Bonn put it (p. 99, *op. cit.*), a tenant redeeming a rent of £100 a year at eighteen years' purchase would become liable for forty-nine years for a payment of 4 per cent on £1,800, i.e. £72, which is £28 a year less than his former rent. "An Irish tenant therefore (by the use of English credit) becomes an owner by the process of paying for forty-nine years a rent 28 per cent less than that of his neighbour who is under a judicially fixed rent."

On page 101 Dr. Bonn comments rather unkindly. "Under these circumstances the purchase policy became naturally an extremely popular one. This popularity however does not imply that the Irish tenant felt within himself the irresistible impulse to become a proprietor—it only proves that he found himself moved by a keen aspiration towards paying 30 per cent less rent than he did before . . . The hunger for property is not so keen with the Irish peasant as has been asserted."

While it is difficult to see how otherwise an unsatisfactory system of land tenure could have been liquidated, it must be admitted that this particular feature of land purchase policy has left a permanent legacy of demoralisation. The desire to get something for nothing, usually at the expense of the general taxpayer, is a widespread human instinct. As we shall see, Land Purchase policy was continued long after the class of alien landlords had been eliminated, and in the post 1932 era has been directed against the owners of the larger holdings, themselves "purchased tenants," with a view to increasing the number of "economic" small holdings. As each new holding thus created is worth from £600 to £1,000 more than the fortunate "allottee" is required to pay for it, the "sky is the limit" to the demand for such holdings, but there is a very strict limit to the amount of available "good earth." The element of bonus involved in such transfers of land is a burden on the general taxpayer to the extent that it is not imposed on the compulsorily expropriated owner in the form of inadequate compensation.

The legal power of the State to acquire large holdings for division among landless men, for relief of congestion, deprives the owners of such holdings of the sense of security of tenure, and undermines their long-term credit with financial institutions (Banking Commission Report, par. 328). As we shall see, there is room for considerable expansion in the employment and productive capacity of existing large holdings, and they are more suitable for modern methods of mechanised cultivation than small holdings can ever be. The present legal position, by lessening the sense of private property, discourages the growth of private enterprise. The true alternative to the unconditional private ownership of natural resources, if its social results are unsatisfactory, is some form of communal control of the use of such resources.

Anyhow, the Ashbourne Act and its immediate successors were effective for their purpose. By March 31, 1902, over two million acres of Irish land had been sold, and the State had advanced nearly £21 millions. The number of peasant owners created was 75,466 (Bonn, p. 99).

The Wyndham Act of 1903 was preceded by a conference of representatives of landlords and tenants, which met in the Mansion House, Dublin, and issued an agreed report, the principles of which were in fact embodied in the new Bill. The annuities of the tenants were to be some 15 to 25 per cent less than their former rents, and the gross income of the landlords was to be reduced by only 10 per cent. The Treasury of the United Kingdom was to fill the gap by means of a bonus.

Under this Act £70 million was advanced for the purchase of seven million acres of land occupied by 195,000 tenants in the twenty-six county area, and £14½ millions for the purchase of 1,220,000 acres of land occupied by 57,000 tenants in Northern Ireland.

A further Land Purchase Act in 1909 transferred 2,273,000 acres to 61,000 tenants in the south, and 140,000 acres to 5,500 tenants in the north. The Land Act of 1923 compulsorily expropriated the surviving landlords in the south, and transferred nearly four million acres to 127,000 tenant purchasers. A similar Act in 1925 completed the process in Northern Ireland by transferring 805,000 acres to 38,500 tenant purchasers.

The total amount of money advanced by the State for the transfer of land in the southern area was £127,165,980 (*Statistical Abstract*, 1946, p. 70), and in the northern area £26,873,800 (*Ulster Year Book*, 1947, p. 58).

As long ago as in 1904 Dr. Bonn foresaw that certain intractable problems would remain even after the completion of land purchase, and certain other problems would be aggravated by some of the incidental effects of the various Land Acts. The Act of 1881 contained a provision forbidding the subdivision of holdings. Subletting for more than an eleven months' term was also forbidden. The subdivision of holdings had, in pre-Famine years, produced the result that 310,436 holdings, or 44·9 per cent of the total number, were of less than 5 acres in area (Bonn, *op. cit.*, p. 46). The failure of the potato crop had a disastrous effect on the occupants of these tiny holdings. By 1901 the number of such holdings was only 62,855 in all Ireland, or 12·2 per cent of the total number, whereas holdings in excess of 15 acres had substantially increased in number. It was felt to be undesirable to allow the process of subdivision to begin again.

And yet, as Bonn points out (p. 158), subdivision of farms is not so much the consequence of laws of equal inheritance (as in France), but sprang rather from the fact that the father had nothing else to leave his children.

Unable since 1881 to subdivide his holding, the small farmer with a numerous family has tended to put his savings in the bank in order to build up a fund for division among the sons and daughters who are destined not to

⋋ succeed to ownership of the land. In the absence of alternative economic outlets, in an area where small farms predominate, most of the children must migrate, usually emigrate, and each outgoing family member is entitled to his share of the financial fund that has been slowly accumulated by the exertions and self-sacrifice of the family as a whole. Until quite lately it was true to say, as Bonn wrote in 1904 (p. 159), that such savings do not arise from a surplus of profits, but from a deficiency of nourishment, and it is still true that want of capital, fruitfully applied to Irish land, is a chronic disease of Irish agriculture. ⋋

If subdivision of small holdings were allowed, and people were content to accept the standard of living that prevailed before the Famine years (and that prevailed in Eastern Europe in the 1930's), rural population would increase. The mere prohibition of subdivision, *in the absence of alternative economic outlets,* is thus a factor promoting rural depopulation and discouraging the "ploughing back of" farming profits into permanent agricultural improvements.

The theoretical solution is, of course, the growth of a suitably dispersed rural industrialism, but even in the absence of such a development it is relevant to point out that more capital suitably invested in Irish farms of all sizes would mean more production, more employment, a rising standard of living for all and a gradually increasing population. That has been the result in a few exceptional localities where agricultural production has been intensified under the leadership of exceptional men, and there is nothing to prevent these exceptional cases from becoming the general rule, except, of course, the scarcity of exceptional men.

Another incidental result of the land legislation was to fix a financial as well as a social gulf between the class of landless labourers and the beneficiaries of the Land Acts. Prior to 1870 the unreformed land tenure system did at least make access to the soil free for all. No capital was needed by the incoming tenant. Once the principle of dual ownership was established (in 1881), and still more so after the tenant had become a tenant purchaser, the capital value of his ownership interest was increased by the capitalised value of the reduction in his annual outgoing by way of rent or annuity. In future there was no other *economic* means of access to farming short of putting down the purchase price of a farm. This not only excluded those who could not find the necessary capital, but also, in many cases, created a situation in which purchasers of land had exhausted their credit as well as their capital, thus leading to further capital starvation of the soil and "extensive rather than intensive" agricultural production.

In the inter-war period it was found possible to secure access to divided up portions of land, subject to the payment of an annuity, but this could hardly be described as an *economic* means of access to farming. The possibility of securing small holdings in this way, at an annual cost which covers only a fraction of the cost to the community of providing them, has led to a most undersirable activity by way of political "wangling."

In his final analysis Dr. Bonn considers that only a vigorous and successful agricultural co-operative movement could tie up the loose ends of the Irish Agricultural order as it emerged from the agrarian and legislative revolution. The movement in Ireland has problems to solve which are not problems at all in other countries. "In other countries (*op. cit.*, p. 101) the State has banded together individuals in village communities of the most varying kinds, and these working in the framework of institutions of historic antiquity have undertaken the administration of matters of common interest—the communal forests, the pastures, the peat bogs. In Ireland all this organization was an affair of the estate, of the landlord or his agent." Legislation liquidated the landlord interest, but did not substitute for the estate any system of "communal organization of Agriculture."

The co-operative movement in Ireland addressed itself successfully to the problem of cheapening production and improving quality. Its greatest success has been in modernising the dairy industry, which is highly concentrated in Limerick and neighbouring counties. But it cannot be said to have established in the country as a whole any system of "communal agricultural organization."

Unlike the nuclear settlements in the Continent of Europe, farm homesteads in Ireland are dispersed. There are great varieties of soil, elevation, orientation and sizes of farms in practically every agricultural region. Modern agricultural techniques are impossible on the small isolated farm, which relies only on its own resources. The local integration of agricultural effort is the major problem awaiting the application of co-operative methods.

In fact, under present conditions it seems evident that if we would establish a suitable economic basis for a worth-while Irish rural civilisation we must have not only co-operation of farmers living in their scattered homesteads, but large-scale co-operative farming units dotted all over the country. Wherever possible such units should make use of the mansions and estates that were formerly associated with Anglo-Irish landlordism. Unfortunately, there are large regions of the country, particularly in the west, where, in deference to local land hunger and in defiance of the modern conditions of low-cost cultivation, the former large estates have been divided up into "economic" holdings which are no longer economic. In many cases also the "big houses" of former days have gone up in smoke—an irreparable loss from a cultural as well as an agricultural point of view. In such cases a less ambitious approach to the problem of integrating local agricultural effort is indicated. Some suggestions for such an approach have recently appeared in the journal of the Young Farmers' Clubs, the "Irish Farmers' Journal," and are contained in the final chapter of this book.

In a paper read to the Statistical and Social Inquiry Society of Ireland on 27th November, 1947, I wrote as follows :—

"There are various points of view from which a con-sideration of the practicability and desirability of fully integrated co-operative farming in Éire might be approached. We must take into account, in the first instance, the rugged inescapable facts; for no sound structure can be erected which is not firmly based on these. These facts are of the most varied character, but broadly speaking they divide themselves into two main groups—facts of Irish human nature as influenced by history and modified by present-day circumstances, and facts of a more objective character, like the facts of climate and geographical situation, and those other facts that concern the application of modern scientific knowledge to the organisational problems and the productive techniques appropriate to modern agriculture.

The accident of history has determined that our 11 million acres of "crops and pasture" should be divided among about 300,000 owners, each one constituting a distinct economic unit legally responsible for his success or failure as a separate economic enterprise. These farm units (for practical purposes we may refer to them as holdings) are of the most varied sizes, the average size being about 30 acres. Farms under 50 acres in size may be referred to as "small," farms 50–100 acres in size may be called "medium," while farms in excess of the 100-acre size may be regarded, from an Irish point of view, as "large," though elsewhere the term "large" would probably relate to a much higher acreage minimum. We may note, in passing, that if we leave out of account all holdings of less than 5 acres, there are 226,000 holdings between 5 and 50 acres in size. They cover an area of 5,246,000 acres, which is 35·3 per cent of the total area of agricultural land given in official statistics. The total area of all holdings exceeding 5 acres in size, namely, 14,822,900 acres, includes some four or five million acres of rough mountain grazing and other land which is, at present, practically useless for agricultural purposes.

There are 50,000 "medium" farms, occupying an area of 3,524,000 acres or 23·7 per cent of the total agricultural area in question. The large holdings number 29,000, and account for 6,103,000 acres, which is 41 per cent of the total agricultural area. Only 7,949 of these large holdings exceed 200 acres in size. The number in excess of 500 acres in size is probably about 1,500.[1]

In many regions of the country, farms of the most varied sizes occur in close juxtaposition. From a map on page lviii of *Agricultural Statistics, 1847–1926*, it will be noted that small farms are the prevalent type in a group of counties from Monaghan to Mayo, including Donegal; medium farms prevail in a group that includes Wexford, Carlow, Kilkenny, Waterford, Cork, Limerick and Clare. In Meath, Westmeath, Offaly, Dublin and Kildare large farms are the more typical.

Elsewhere in this most valuable official publication it is pointed out and proved statistically that there is an important agricultural commerce, binding together farms of

---

[1] Cf. App. I, p. 93, *Majority Report of Committee of Inquiry on Post-Emergency Agricultural Policy.*

various sizes and various productive possibilities, and that this commerce takes place regionally as well as locally, thus transforming the appearance of isolated and independent farm units into the substance of a national agricultural economy. The question is, would the introduction of large-scale co-operative farming units in every characteristic farming area of the country promote an even closer integration of the national agricultural effort in a regional as well as a national sense? Would it eliminate some of the wastes incidental to the present system, e.g. the transporting of half-starved Limerick calves through two or three counties before they find a temporary resting place? Would such a system promote more effective use of local human and material resources, and therefore make possible a greater output of wealth and a higher standard of living for all? The answer to this question must depend partly on the possibilities of Irish human nature and the availability of suitable agricultural leadership, conscious of a mission, able to appeal to the emotions as well as to the intellect, and capable of harnessing all spiritual and material resources in an effort to achieve a social order in which the individual can fully realise his best self because his welfare is merged in the welfare of a community of individuals. All we can do in the course of this paper is to point out that such developments, however Utopian they may sound, would in fact only be a logical development of certain features of our agricultural economy *that now exist,* and a desirable rationalisation of those aspects of it which are indefensible economically and therefore anti-social in effect.

The number of males "engaged" in farm work on the 1st June, 1944, was 526,000 (*Statistical Abstract,* 1945, Table 57). It was 579,000 in 1934 (*Statistical Abstract,* 1939, Table 53). The total area of crops and pasture is officially given as 11,703,000 acres (*Agricultural Statistics,* 1927–1933, Table 6), and the total agricultural area, which includes "other land," as 17,024,000 acres. If we take the 1944 figure for males "engaged" in farm work (526,000) and apply it to the figure indicating total agricultural area (17,024,000 acres) the average for the whole country works out at rather more than 3 males engaged for every 100 acres of agricultural area. It would work out at 4·5 for every 100 acres of crops and pasture.

Using the data contained in Appendix II on page 94 of the *Post Emergency Committee's Majority Report on Agricultural Policy,* it appears that there were in 1936 386,000 males "engaged" on farms from 1 acre to 50 acres in size. The total area of the farms in this group is officially given as 5,522,000 acres. Thus there are seven males "engaged" in agriculture for every 100 acres of "agricultural area" in farms under 50 acres in size. In our definition of "small" farms we left out the size group 1–5 acres, but for our present purposes we may regard a density of 7 persons "engaged" per 100 acres of farm area as sufficiently typical of the small-farm category of our definition. The density per 100 acres of crops and pasture would, of course, work out at about 10.

In the "medium" farms man-power in 1936 was 119,000 and total area 3,547,000 acres. In this category man-power per 100 acres of total area works out at 3·35.

In the "large" farms of our definition, man-power was (in 1936) 92,700 and total area 5,936,000 acres. The ratio of man-power to total acreage was in this category 1·56 to 100 acres. Incidentally, it may be noted that, according to Mr. Freeman's calculations, there was a slight tendency for man-power to increase between 1926 and 1936 on farms between 30 and 200 acres in size, but a 5·6 per cent decrease in farms 15 to 30 acres, and a 20 per cent decrease in farms 1 to 15 acres in size.[2]

One of our major economic problems is to increase the density of agricultural employment as well as output per person and per acre on our agricultural area as a whole. During the 1930's the political and economic atmosphere was distinctly unhealthy for the large holding, especially those of the "rancher" class. And yet large holdings up to 200 acres in size maintained and even increased the man-power associated with them, while the decrease of some 3,000 associated with farms over 200 acres in size was adequately accounted for by the public policy that promoted the division of such holdings. Economic tendencies, if left to themselves, would probably promote a further consolidation of holdings, and the total number of holdings under 50 acres would probably diminish, in spite of the

[2] See App. II, p. 94, *Majority Report on Agricultural Policy by Committee on Post-Emergency Agricultural Policy.*

artificial creation of new holdings under 30 acres in size by the Land Commission. Yet a policy of *laissez-faire* in this matter is politically impossible and perhaps socially undesirable. The path of wisdom is to work with the tide in promoting suitable consolidations of holdings in convenient centres while at the same time taking care that the public good is nowhere subordinate to private selfish interests. It may be that an experiment in the establishment of large-scale co-operative farming units, under public auspices but not under public control, will provide a solution in accordance with democratic principles and the ideals of a Christian social order.

The relative densities of man-power per 100 acres of area, namely, 7, 3·35, and 1·56 in small, medium and large farms respectively, appear to afford an argument for dividing up the land into the smallest possible units. However, output per person, on which the standard of life depends, almost certainly varies directly with the size of farm, as well as with other factors, some of which are within the control of the human will. A chess-board pattern of nothing but small farms would lose even the present limited degree of mutual interdependence between small, medium and large farms which is one of the essential characteristics of a national agricultural economy. In fact, a congeries of small farmers not co-operatively associated with one another for production, processing, buying, or selling, would be a kind of agricultural slum and in no sense a rural community.

To a certain extent the economic isolation of our individual farm units has been qualified by the application of co-operative methods to many of their common interests. The most successful example of this in Éire is in connection with the Creamery industry. Moreover, the Creamery Societies perform a lot of functions for their members which are not directly related to the making and sale of butter. In the non-creamery districts co-operative association is comparatively undeveloped. But hitherto the co-operative method has not been applied on any large scale to the general processes of production on actual farms, though there have been one or two attempts to do so, and more recently the purchase of large farms by some of our wealthier and more enterprising creameries has provided the possibility of ambitious developments in this direction.

Large-scale farming can be just as intensive as small-scale farming. It can concentrate on aspects of agricultural production and processing which cannot be done economically in a small farm or cannot be done at all. According to an English authority, D. B. Johnstone-Wallace, as reported in *The Farmers' Weekly* of January 28, 1944: 'To be fully equipped a 100 acre arable dairy farm now requires a medium-powered tractor, a power-lift toolbar with hoes and cultivator tines, a direct-attached mower for the tractor, a two-furrow plough with general purpose and digger bodies, a spike-tooth harrow, a Cambridge roller, a fertiliser distributor, a combine grain-drill also adapted for root crops, a power-drive binder, a combined swath turner and side-delivery rake, a horse rake, a tractor sweep, two pneumatic-tyred carts, two low-loading dumping trailers, a steam sterilizer, a milk-cooler, and various small tools. In addition, it would be helpful to have a milking machine, a 5–7½ H.P. electric motor, an electric refrigerating plant for cooling and storing milk, a double-disc harrow, a flexible grass harrow, etc.'

Obviously the typical Irish farm of 50 to 100 acres is not and cannot be fully equipped in this sense. And yet the low-cost production of tillage crops is not possible unless on farms which are fully equipped with the most up-to-date labour economising machinery. According to some authorities, the economic growing of corn crops is virtually restricted to farms of at least 350 acres in size.

On farms over 100 acres in area the ratio of man-power per 100 acres of area is, as we have seen, 1·56. On several individual large farms with which I am acquainted 10 persons or more per 100 acres are fully and productively engaged. On a well-known 2,000 acre mixed tillage farm in the Midlands 100 workers are permanently employed—a ratio of 5 persons to 100 acres. The question is—Can we reproduce under a co-operative system the technical and other conditions which enable our best-managed, privately-owned large holdings to show a high density of employment and a high output per man and per acre? We cannot tell unless a few large-scale experiments are made, adequately financed and under suitable leadership.''

The success of any such experiments would depend on local initiative and the quality of local leadership. But a new orientation of State-sponsored agricultural policy and some alteration of existing Land Acts would also be highly desirable if not essential.

The Land Act of 1923 made provision for the compulsory transfer to tenant purchasers of the land not voluntarily sold under former Acts. The Land Act of 1933 was directed, not at the former landlords who had ceased to exist as a class, but at the owners of large farms, themselves usually "purchased" tenants. It conferred on the Land Commission the power compulsorily to acquire land without any reference to the relief of congestion and to transfer it to anyone it thought fit within the terms of a wide legal definition.

The Banking Commission in its Report (pars. 502 ff.) expressed disapproval of these powers, and criticised the manner in which they were being exercised. Putting it mildly, it considered that the powers of the Land Commission were not being exercised with due regard to the "wider economic implications of the policy being pursued" (par. 507).

But these powers, however wide, are in some respects not wide enough. The Land Commission has legal power compulsorily to acquire any large farm, but having acquired it, it must divide it up and transfer it to a number of individual small holders, each one of whom, if formerly landless, is provided with a new house and farm buildings, largely at the expense of the State. A truncated area of ornamental and generally useless land is left around the former mansion, whose elaborate farm buildings now bear no appropriate relation to the diminished area of the surrounding farm, and are practically useless. In creating new farm units of doubtful value the Land Commission incidentally destroys the economic value of mansions and farm buildings, which would be of immense social, cultural, and economic value in a rationally ordered rural society.

The Land Commission does not transfer large holdings complete with mansion and farm buildings, to co-operative societies of farmers or workers for operation as a single unit, or indeed rarely to any collective entity whatever. In this respect at least its legal powers, if inadequate, ought to be widened.

CHAPTER II

NOWADAYS, the principal official agent of agricultural policy is the Department of Agriculture, and the principal semi-official agent is the Irish Agricultural Organisation Society. These institutions have an interesting historical background, and both of them are imperishably associated with the life-long self-sacrificing idealism of the late Sir Horace Plunkett.

A younger son of the sixteenth Baron Dunsany, Horace Plunkett was born on October 24, 1854. His subsequent career was by no means typical of the class of fox-hunting squires into which he was born. In 1874 he entered University College, Oxford, and read the Honours School of Modern History, in which he obtained a Second in 1877. As Margaret Digby points out in her valuable biography of Plunkett,[3] it was at this period that he became inspired with a vague social idealism. He was not happy about the impact of the Industrial Revolution on the social economy of England. While he welcomed the new techniques that modern science made available for agriculture as well as for industry, he feared the effect of the cruder forms of commercial capitalism on the rural scene in Ireland.

Owing to ill-health, which necessitated long periods of absence in the U.S.A., it was nearly twenty years before this almost unconscious dedication of his life was able to manifest itself in appropriate action. He had become interested in the Consumers' Co-operative movement in England, and he saw the possibility of applying the co-operative idea to the problem of saving the Irish butter trade. Irish butter made by primitive methods on the farm, and by no means uniform or reliable in quality, was being driven from the British market by the co-operatively processed high-grade product of other countries. It was an uphill fight to win the confidence of the Irish dairy farmers. As a member of the "Ascendancy class" his political motives were suspect.

[3] "Horace Plunkett: An Anglo-American Irishman."

Vested interests were concerned with the traditional butter trade, and they did not scruple to appeal to high-sounding political "ideologies." One worthy said that every pound of butter made in Rathkeale must be made on Nationalist principles or not at all. The first co-operative creamery was started in 1889. There were seventeen by 1891, and they were already a proved success.

In 1891 Arthur Balfour, then Chief Secretary, offered Plunkett a seat on the Congested Districts Board which he established in that year. He accepted, and remained a member for many years; but he could not throw his whole heart into the work of that Board. Actually, the C.D.B., or the "Congested Board" (to use its popular name), functioned from 1891 till 1923, and did a valuable work of agricultural and industrial education and land resettlement in the over-populated western regions. It resembled the Tennessee Valley Authority in the flexibility of its methods and its freedom from "Treasury control." Its history has been written by the late W. L. Micks. Sir Horace Plunkett writing in 1915 said : "The Congested Districts, where the Board's land purchase operations are advanced, are marvellously improved. The great defect I see is the utter ignoring of the social aspects of the problem. No attempt is made to build up rural communities."

In 1894 he founded the Irish Agricultural Organization Society. This is the permanent organizing and supervising institution in connection with the movement for agricultural co-operation. It was unique so far as Ireland was concerned, in the sense that its membership and governing committee contained persons of all religions and diverse political views. Under Plunkett's benevolent leadership, and inspired by the magnetism of his personal character, the Society maintained its "non-political and non-sectarian" character, and no internal discords disturbed its harmony. The political separation of Northern Ireland in 1922 necessitated the creation of a separate Ulster Agricultural Organization Society, but the two Irish Societies continue to maintain friendly and fraternal relations.

In 1892 Plunkett had become a Member of Parliament for South County Dublin. Though nominally a Member of the Unionist Party, he was essentially a free-lance, and he used his position in order to establish contacts that

might further his ideals for the reconstruction of Irish rural
society.

In 1895 the second Home Rule Bill was defeated, and
in that year a Unionist Government took office with a large
majority.   In the political vacuum occasioned by the
temporary eclipse of the Home Rule movement, and
intensified by the Parnell split, Plunkett got together leading
members of both Irish political parties in the famous Recess
Committee, which reported in 1896.   Its principal recommendation was for the establishment of an all-Irish Department of Agricultural and Technical Instruction under a
Minister responsible to Parliament.   In 1899 a Bill
establishing such a Department was introduced and passed.

So far as agriculture was concerned, the function of the
new Department was to promote agricultural education by
a system of local itinerant instructors, by maintaining
Demonstration Plots, by encouraging and subsidising local
Agricultural Shows, etc., etc.   In Plunkett's opinion, and
that of the Recess Committee, voluntary organization in
local co-operative societies should precede and accompany
State provided attempts at agricultural improvement.   "All
attempts of the Central Government to act through un-
organized individuals, in schemes of agricultural and
industrial improvement, are by implication condemned as
likely to do more harm than good" (Recess Committee
Report, p. 69).   Elsewhere he expressed the view that State
aid should be used to "evoke and supplement," but never so
as to replace local voluntary initiative.

Plunkett was, of course, the first Vice-President of the
new Department, of which the Chief Secretary was the
nominal head.   He entered on office on November 2, 1899.
Unfortunately, he lost his Parliamentary seat in the election
of 1900, but by common consent he carried on as Vice-
President till 1907 when, under the new Liberal Government,
he was replaced by T. W. Russell.   Relations between the
Department and the I.A.O.S. were harmonious so long as
Plunkett, who became Sir Horace Plunkett in 1903, was
head of both.   The finance of the I.A.O.S. came partly from
affiliation fees paid by member societies, partly from
individual subscriptions and partly from the personal
generosity of Sir Horace Plunkett himself.   It was not until
1906 that he was able to secure a direct grant of £3,700

from the State to add to the resources of the I.A.O.S. But under his Vice-Presidency it was clearly recognised that the Department should leave the I.A.O.S. unfettered in its work of organizing the farmers for business purposes. To promote "better farming" was the special function of the Department. To promote "better business" was the legitimate sphere of the I.A.O.S. The crowning objective of "better living" was not so well articulated or clearly defined, but it, too, has long had an organization dedicated to its furtherance—the Irish Countrywomen's Association.

The new Vice-President, Sir Thomas Russell, was very much influenced by the Nationalist Parliamentary Party of those days, and the latter was very much under the sway of local shopkeeping interests. Under pressure from the latter the subsidy was withdrawn from the I.A.O.S. in 1908, but it was restored in 1913 from the "Development Grant" (in spite of the opposition of Sir Thomas Russell) and maintained as long as the British connection lasted.

The work of organising Irish farmers for business purposes was interrupted by the first World War, and still more seriously impeded by the "troubled" years that led to the Anglo-Irish Treaty of 1921. Under the new régime the attitude of the new Minister for Agriculture (the late Paddy Hogan) was one of practical helpfulness. While evading any public declaration in favour of the Three Betters, he made available a subsidy of £10,000 a year, which he considered was worth all the propaganda he could do (Margaret Digby, op. cit., p. 277). The subsidy is still continued at more or less the same annual rate, and, in fact, constitutes more than half the available annual funds of the Society. This continued dependence on funds provided by the taxpayer, on the part of nearly 100,000 organised farmers, whose annual trade turnover now exceeds £20,000,000, suggests certain reflections.

Plunkett was interested in the material improvement of the economic conditions of Irish farmers, but such material improvement was not his primary concern. He realised that the State had an important part to play in this connection. The abolition of landlordism removed one of the principal obstacles to material improvement. This was a purely negative contribution on the part of the State. It was also the duty of the State to provide adequate education and expert advice. But, as Æ. used to say, the experts must always be on tap and never on top. The real dynamic must be "self help through mutual help," and the search for economic betterment by this means would incidentally create a social order of mutual helpfulness, thus bringing the blessings of the Industrial Revolution to Irish Agriculture uncontaminated by its curse.

In 1904 Plunkett published his "Ireland in the New Century." It contains many of his wisest and wittiest epigrams and an appreciation of the Irish national character, in which he says that the Irishman "treats life as if he were a mere sojourner on earth whose true home is somewhere else ... What the Irishman is really attached to in Ireland is not a home but a social order—the pleasant amenities, the courtesies, the leisureliness, the associations of religion and the friendly faces of the neighbours."

The practical necessity of maintaining its non-political, non-sectarian character added to the difficulty of developing the idealistic side of the movement and integrating its social philosophy with what we may call the national soul. Standish O'Grady wrote: "I do think that a certain conscious idealization of the movement is desirable even towards its material success. How exactly that idealization is to be secured is no doubt a difficult question. I shall endeavour to think the matter out." The matter still requires thinking out.

Nearly forty years ago I remember impassioned pleas by the late R. A. Anderson, the late Harold Barbour, and the late George Russell (Æ.), advocating a mighty effort to make the movement financially self-supporting and completely independent of State aid. If it made one tithe of the emotional appeal to its members and beneficiaries that an ordinary political party, Trade Union or Football Club can command, its present annual income would be much more than £20,000, and all of it would be provided by the affiliated societies.

The present material position of the movement may be judged from the following facts. There were in 1948 197 Creamery Societies operating in 457 different processing units. The membership of these societies was 50,597, the paid-up share capital £432,070, loan capital £569,544, and trade turnover £17,268,700. Of so-called Agricultural

Societies there were 73, with a membership of 22,975, a paid-up share capital of £98,464, a loan capital of £204,534, and a trade turnover of £2,108,916. So-called miscellaneous societies were 20 in number with a membership of 20,446. Paid-up share capital amounted to £184,966, loan capital to £102,904, and trade turnover to £1,598,200. One Wholesale Society had 359 federated society members, a paid-up share capital of £36,662, and used a loan capital of £270,413. Creamery Society membership was a little more than half the total of organised farmers, but accounted for nearly 70 per cent of total trade turnover.

The co-operative creameries thus constitute by far the most important element in the Irish Agricultural Co-operative movement as a whole. This implies a geographical limitation which also militates against the national character of the movement. For creameries can only function where farmers are relatively specialised for dairy farming. There are six south-western counties and five north-western counties in the twenty-six county area in which the number of cows per 100 acres of crops and pasture is 10 or more. These are the Creamery Counties. The map at the end of this book, which Dr. Kennedy of the I.A.O.S. kindly prepared, illustrates the present geographical distribution of creamery and other co-operative societies.

The movement as a whole may now be regarded as a semi-official agency of Government Agricultural Policy in close association with the Department of Agriculture, which is the regular official agency. At the same time it cannot be regarded as entirely dominated by the State. It operates as a very effective pressure group, as will be indicated in the following pages, and its democratic organisation gives it a vote organising potential which causes both the great political parties to treat it with respect. Actually, there are prominent co-operative leaders in both parties, and neither party would willingly make a present to the other of all the goodwill and political influence which such a large movement could command, if it entered the political arena as a self-conscious political organisation. There are good, practical reasons for having powerful friends in both camps, but they are of a material order, and in adapting itself to the realities of party politics in an independent Ireland, the movement as a whole, if it has not quite lost its soul, has

abdicated some of the loftier functions which Sir Horace
Plunkett and his associates regarded as its highest objective.

Most of the members of the 197 Creamery Societies appear
to be more interested in maintaining a State subsidised
artificially high price for milk than in reducing the cost of
producing it by eliminating uneconomic cows and feeding
more adequately and scientifically those that remain in their
herds.   But there are a dozen or a score of these Societies
which have shown real enterprise, and by embarking on the
ownership and cultivation of model farms have educated
their members in the principles of better farming as well as
better business.   In some cases these experiments may tend
to the promotion of a new social order, in which better
living will be a reality and no longer a vague dream.   But
in general the spiritual ferment that is now going on in the
Irish countryside is represented by the very vigorous Young
Farmers' Club movement and other kindred organisations.
These are by no means confined to the Creamery Counties,
though well represented there also.

It may be that the missing link is a failure to provide
the right kind of education for the Irish countryman and
countrywoman in their youth.   Ever since its foundation,
Agricultural Education has been a special function of the
"Department."   In the estimates for 1947–48 £64,327 are
provided for State-owned Agricultural Schools and Farms,
including the famous Albert Agricultural College at Glasnevin, which is now an organic part of the National University.
In addition, private Agricultural Schools, most of them
operated by religious orders, are subsidised to the extent of
£21,827.   The faculty of Dairy Science in Cork got £13,000
in 1947–48.   The County Council Committees of Agriculture
maintain itinerant instructors, who hold winter agricultural
classes for adult farmers, and give practical advice on the
farm to those seeking it.   This is the most important aspect
of practical agricultural education, and in 1947–48 the
State contributed £209,470 to the cost of this service.   In 1945
the number of students attending Courses in Agriculture in
State provided Agricultural Schools and Colleges was 821, and
in State subsidised private Agricultural Schools it was 756.
There is reason to believe that most of these very limited
numbers of students qualify for white-collar occupations
afterwards, and that very few of them become "dirty boots"
farmers on their own or any other person's farm.

*In 1857 there were 160 Agricultural Schools, including
73 "Workhouse" Schools, in Ireland with model farms of
various sizes attached. In 38 of them 191 residential
boarders were accommodated; other pupils receiving whole-
time practical instruction in Agriculture numbered 2,933.
The total cost to the State was £8,237 19s. 2d.*

In addition, a diminishing, but still substantial, proportion of Teachers in Training of all religions was boarded
at the Albert Model Farm and took part in its work.   In
their subsequent teaching career many of these men became
centres of agricultural enlightenment in every one of the
32 counties of Ireland.   As will be explained later, this
educational system was seriously impaired by a British
Treasury decision of 1875, but a remnant of it lingered on till
the end of the century. *Fifty years ago it was completely
disrupted and has never since been revived.*   Practically all
the pupils attending Agricultural Schools in the mid-
nineteenth century were destined to become farm labourers,
farm stewards, and farmers.   There were few white-collar
occupations open to agricultural students in those days.
The information on which these statements are based is
derived in part from a book called "Mixed Education: The
Catholic Case Stated" (p. 340 ff.), published in 1859 by John
Mullany, Dublin.   The author calls himself "A Catholic
Layman."

Nowadays the important part of our practical agricultural education is what is given in winter agricultural
classes for adult students, and in the course of visits by the
itinerant instructors to farmers on their farms.   The
tragedy is that the general education of most farmers has been
so defective, and so lacking in a scientific basis, that they are
unable to take full advantage of the teaching made available,
even if they have the sense to realise that they need it.
The irony is that the Department, by reason of its special
interest in agricultural education, provided an occasion or
excuse for breaking with the valuable tradition, referred
to above, which was in its heyday in the middle of the
nineteenth century, and still lingered on when the Recess
Committee was reporting in 1896. "In this respect, the
National Board of Education must be freed from a reproach
under which it has unjustly been allowed to lie.   At an
early stage of its existence the National Board made an
earnest and extensive endeavour to diffuse a knowledge of

agricultural science among the people . . . So far back as
1838, the Model Farm at Glasnevin, which is now known as
the Albert National Agricultural Training Institution,
was established with a view to the training in Agriculture
of National Teachers, so that a course of practical agricultural instruction might be engrafted upon the ordinary
curriculum of the elementary schools." (Recess Committee
Report, p. 7).

In the year 1850 there were eleven Model Agricultural
Schools (under the exclusive management of the Board).
In addition, there were twelve Model Agricultural Schools
under local management but recognized by the Board.
There were also 36 ordinary agricultural schools, that is to
say, National Schools, with two acres or more of land
attached, in which the pupils received practical instruction
in agriculture as well as a general primary education. The
farms attached to the Model Schools varied from 7 to 178
acres in size, and residential boarders were accommodated in
the school buildings. In the year 1875 the number of State
managed Model Schools was 19, locally managed Model
Schools 11, and ordinary Agricultural Schools 175—i.e. a
total of 205 apart from "Workhouse" schools. But in that
year a fanatical English Free Trade Association, which
"disputed the right of the State to train up farmers and
stewards at the public cost," persuaded the Treasury to
wield the axe, and the Board reluctantly abandoned most
of its activities of this character. That public opinion in
Ireland favoured the scheme of primary education, thus
ruthlessly suppressed, is stated in the Recess Report, and
is also evident from the fact that 30,000 copies of a very
practical manual of agriculture, for use in these Model
Schools, were sold within two years of its publication in
1867.

It was an essential part of the educational scheme
referred to that many of the teachers in training should live
at the Glasnevin Model Farm, absorb its atmosphere and
take part in its work, while pursuing their more general
education at the Marlborough Street Training College.

Even after the Treasury decision of 1875 a trace of the
former system still persisted. As late as 1893 there still
remained 45 ordinary Agricultural Schools with small farms
attached, and 30 schools with cottage gardens attached.

The Recess Committee gratefully noted the fact that the National Board was still carrying on the Albert Model Farm in Glasnevin, and giving a six-weeks' course of agricultural training to a proportion of National School teachers. Agriculture was still taught in the National Schools as a theoretical subject, and a well-known text-book of agriculture (not the one referred to above) was still in common use. The Recess Committee recommended that this education should be continued in the primary schools, and made practical in every case by association with Demonstration Plots in cases where school gardens or small farms were not available.

This important recommendation of the Recess Committee was not implemented by the Department. What happened was that all agricultural education was dropped by the National Board from the curriculum of the primary schools, and the whole business of agricultural education was left to the Department, which could never fill this gap.

In recent years there has been a development of Rural Science Classes as part of the Vocational Educational Scheme of the Department of Education. But the wound inflicted by the Treasury decision of 1875 and the decision of the National Board in the early 1900's has never yet been fully healed. The failure to integrate general education with agricultural education in rural Ireland is an important cause of our agricultural deficiencies and a serious handicap to the would-be creators of a new social order. *In this vital respect a most important recommendation of the Recess Committee still remains to be implemented.*

While it is desirable that agricultural education should become more closely integrated with general education, it is well to recognise that it may no longer be feasible to integrate it with general education at the primary stage. During the nineteenth century it was customary for considerable numbers of pupils to continue in attendance at a primary school up to an advanced age. In 1890 the total number on the rolls of all primary schools in Ireland was 1,037,102, and of these, 53,810 exceeded the age of fifteen years. At that age they would be well able to take part in the practical work of a model farm. In 1947–48 there were 457,052 pupils on the rolls of primary schools in the Eire area. Of these only 4,815 boys and 8,643 girls exceeded the age of fourteen years—a much smaller proportion than before.

Actually, what the present situation requires is a great extension of secondary education amongst the rural population, and a close integration of agricultural with general education at the secondary stage. Only at that stage is it feasible to provide the groundwork of chemical and biological knowledge on which alone an efficient system of agricultural education can be built. Agricultural instruction, in the absence of such a scientific groundwork, may have its uses, but it cannot be regarded as *educational*.

In 1936 there were about 410,000 boys and girls in our area between the ages of twelve and nineteen. The number between the ages of twelve and twenty who were in attendance at secondary schools in 1936–37 was 36,000. In addition there were 17,000 students under sixteen, and 48,000 students over sixteen at Vocational Schools. It is quite evident that the vast majority of our boys and girls get no secondary education at all. As a matter of fact, most of them, especially in the rural areas, cease to attend the primary school at or before the age of fourteen years.

Some of our existing secondary schools are provided with farms which could easily be turned into Model or Demonstration Farms. The College of St. Columba, near Dublin, has been a pioneer in this respect. When the attention of the Minister of Agriculture was drawn to the significance of its work it was immediately recognised as qualified to secure the appropriate educational grant. St. Columba's is a Protestant School. It is highly desirable that its example in this matter should be followed by other schools, whatever their religious auspices, which, having farms attached, are in a position to develop a department of practical and theoretical agricultural education.

CHAPTER III

AGRICULTURAL POLICY AFTER 1922

IT is convenient to summarise at this stage the agricultural policy, apart from the question of land tenure, that was pursued by the national Government after 1922. From that date, two Governments—in fact three—functioned in Ireland, and it is no longer possible to speak of a single Agricultural policy applied to Ireland as a whole. The subsequent history of agriculture in Northern Ireland is a separate story, which it was only possible to glance at occasionally, by way of contrast and comparison, in the course of the following pages. Northern Ireland remained an integral part of the United Kingdom, and therefore was not affected prejudicially by the Economic War of 1932–1938. During the second World War that country profited by the more favourable price policy which was applied to United Kingdom farmers, and made a creditable contribution to the national larder. The economic circumstances of the southern area were completely different, and as much of the matter contained in this book was derived from personal contacts and personal experiences on the south side of the Border, it seemed preferable to attempt no comprehensive treatment of agricultural developments in Northern Ireland.

The establishment of a national Government in 1922 involved no serious interruption in officially sponsored agricultural policies in the south. Until 1926, when a census of agricultural output was taken, it is difficult to give an account of developments with quantitative precision. However, until 1932, when Mr. De Valera's Government took office, the policy was to specialise in the production of livestock and livestock products. The area under corn crops declined from a maximum of 1,456,000 acres in 1918 to 760,000 acres in 1932, and this represented most of the decline that took place in tillage in these years. When, however, we take account of the total output in terms of starch tons of corn, root and green crops and hay, we find a decline from 2,764,900 tons in 1918 to 2,410,000 tons in 1934—a decline of much smaller proportions. Meanwhile the area under grass had increased as the area under the plough diminished, and, although no exact estimate is available of the starch tons of feed available from this additional acreage, it is interesting to note that, according to Professor Duncan's calculations,[4] the physical volume of our total agricultural production increased in the ratio of 94 to 101 between 1926 and 1931. The tendency to increase specialisation in livestock and livestock products is indicated by the increase from 86 per cent in 1926–27 to 89 per cent in 1929–30 of the proportion of output so constituted.

However, the advent of Mr. De Valera's Government in 1932, and the almost simultaneous outbreak of the Economic War with the United Kingdom, reversed this tendency. The official policy now was to speed the plough at all costs, and encourage, by a system of guaranteed prices and import restrictions, the growing of food crops for human consumption in the home market, especially wheat and beet. By 1938 the proportion of agricultural output that took the form of such "cash crops" had increased from about one-tenth to about one-sixth. However, total agricultural output, after a temporary spurt, began to show a downward trend, and in 1938 was only 98 per cent of its volume in 1929. Between 1934 and 1938 the "Banking Commission" was in session. The fact that it was set up at all indicated perhaps a certain misgiving about the wisdom of national economic policy as a whole, and its Report in 1938 coincided significantly with the settlement of the Economic War, and seemed likely to lead to a modification of agricultural policy in the direction of greater emphasis on livestock and livestock products. There was no time for any such modification to show results before the outbreak of the second World War compelled our Government to do from necessity what it had formerly done from choice, and concentrate once more on growing crops for direct human consumption regardless of the long-term effect on the fertility of the soil. In the interval our Government had probably learnt that its effort to promote a tillage economy, based on a declining and semi-bankrupt animal husbandry, was disintegrating the national economy as a whole and

[4] See page 41.

destroying the natural fertility of our soil. But the outbreak of the World War made it impossible to apply the
lessons learned in the expensive school of Economic War,
and our agriculture entered the arena of the World War
"emergency" already bruised and battered by its recent
experience.

In the circumstances, the fact that it was able to make
the contribution it did make to the national larder between
1939 and 1945 was most surprising. Practically no imports
of potassic and phosphatic fertilisers were obtainable after
1941, and the country had been economising in artificial
manures ever since 1932. Imported feed stuffs also had to
be dispensed with. Quantitatively these amount, as a rule,
only to about one-sixth of the total available supplies of
tillage products used as raw material for our animal
husbandry. The other five-sixths are tillage products of
domestic origin. But the imported product complements
the home-grown product, thus balancing the ration. Owing
to the absence of the imported complement there must have
been much waste of home-grown materials during the war.
Including an estimate of the cereal equivalent derived from
pasture and hay, the total available raw materials for
animal husbandry diminished from 9,905,000 cereal tons in
1932 to 8,176,000 tons in 1943. The diminution in the output
of livestock and livestock products was in much the same
proportion.

It is common knowledge that the highest yields, even of
crops for direct human consumption, are obtainable only by
those countries whose climate and circumstances enable them
to place chief emphasis on animal husbandry. Our climate
is ideally suitable for the production of grass, the cheapest
of all sources of animal feed. But the circumstances
associated with the Economic War and the British price
policy inaugurated in 1934, which discouraged the winter
fattening of Irish cattle in the stalls, diminished the supply
of farmyard manure and destroyed the possibility of
expanding tillage for human consumption without lessening
yields and impairing soil fertility. The divorce between
animal husbandry and cash-crop production began during
the Economic War, persisted all through the second World
War because its principal cause, the British differential
price policy, was maintained. It was abandoned only in
1948. Thus we were compelled by external circumstances

to plough up an increasing acreage of pasture land in order
to obtain a grain supply, the total of which failed to increase
in equal proportions and was always inadequate. A million
acres of pasture land were sacrificed in the process.
Inevitably the output of milk and cattle suffered. In
1929/30 we exported 51·4 per cent of total agricultural
output, consisting almost entirely of livestock and livestock
products. In 1942/43 the percentage exported was 23·5.
If our exports of butter and bacon were non-existent during
most of the war years and our exports of cattle diminished
from 775,000 in 1929 to 484,000 in 1947, the principal causes
are those indicated or suggested in the following pages, and
not all of them are the direct responsibility of an Irish
Government.

Meanwhile the idea began to penetrate even the highest
circles that perhaps there was something to be said for an
agricultural policy that worked with nature instead of
against her. In 1942 a Committee, of which the present
writer was a member, was appointed "to consider and report
on the measures best calculated to provide for the situation
which may be expected to exist in the agricultural industry
at the end of the Emergency, with special reference to
measures for increasing the fertility of the land, promoting
efficiency in the industry and making the various branches
of the industry self-supporting."

Its Majority Report on Agricultural Policy was published in 1945. Its recommendation of a policy of ley
farming was a happy blend of "plough speeding" and livestock specialisation ideologies, which enabled it to be adopted
by the late Government and still more enthusiastically by
the present Inter-party Government.

The fact that there is now substantial agreement between
Government and Opposition on the objectives of our
agricultural policy must be attributed in some degree to the
work of this Committee. The masterly exposition of the
technique of ley farming contained in the Majority Report
owes much to the knowledge and practical experience of
Mr. Robert Barton, a former signatory of the Anglo-Irish
Treaty of 1921, and a supporter of Mr. De Valera, who ceased
to take an active part in politics when he became Chairman
of the Agricultural Corporation.

The present writer may also say with reference to this
Report—"CUJUS PARS PARVA FUI."

CHAPTER IV

RAW MATERIALS FOR IRISH ANIMAL HUSBANDRY

THERE are three possible objectives for agricultural production. One may produce cash crops for direct human consumption. This, of course, involves tillage. One may produce animal products also for human consumption. In those few countries in which grass will grow readily this in some form—as grass, as hay, or as silage—is the cheapest of all raw materials for animal product production. But tillage is also necessary in order to supplement the deficiencies of grass—fresh or preserved—as winter feed for cattle, and also in order to provide food for those animals—e.g. pigs, which can only make use of grass to a limited extent. The tillage need not necessarily take place on a farm which specialises in animal products, but the products of tillage must be available from some source, native or external, if such a farm is to specialise in animal product production. The third possible objective of agricultural activity is the production of raw material for industry. The growing of cotton, jute, or flax are typical examples of the third objective. Agriculture in Éire is only concerned to a limited extent with this form or production, but in Northern Ireland the growing of flax is quite important. There are a few areas in Éire also in which flax is grown.

The primary object of the first two forms of agriculture is the production of human food. But bye-products or joint products, which become raw materials for industry, are incidentally produced, for example, hides and wool. The converse also takes place. Cotton-seed oil is an important bye-product of cotton growing. It is also possible to grow flax for the production of linseed as well as fibre.

Irish agriculture is concerned mainly with the first two forms, and, traditionally, more disposed to produce animal products than cash crops for direct human consumption. Nature has clothed the Emerald Isle in a garment of grass

D

and there are only a few areas in which it is *essential* to till the soil regularly in order to keep that garment fresh and green.   According to modern scientific opinion there are only a few areas in which it would not be *desirable* to "take the plough round the farm," and assist nature by treating grass as a crop well worthy of cultivation.

In regions where grass of some sort will persist from year to year it is possible to have a cattle or sheep economy with little or no cultivation of the soil apart from hay-making. But if the cattle are to be adequately fed in the winter time, and other more intensive forms of animal husbandry practised, e.g. pig or poultry production, it is not possible to proceed without using the products of tillage husbandry conducted somewhere or other.

Broadly speaking, the production of cash crops, e.g. wheat, is an important feature of overseas agriculture, while animal husbandry tends to become the main agricultural activity of Western European countries.

If the object of agriculture *was* merely to provide a maximum of subsistence with a minimum of labour there would, in the world as a whole, be less animal husbandry, and in fact less cultivation of the soil than there normally is. For much of the cultivation that takes place in time of peace (if such a time can be called normal) *is* with a view to providing food for animals in some country or other.

The pig is the most economical transformer of cereal raw materials into high-class human food, but even the pig requires about 4 lbs. of a balanced cereal ration to produce 1 lb. of pig (live weight).   Millions of human beings have in recent years learnt to subsist on the cereal products which in happier times were fed to hens and pigs, and there are hundreds of millions of Asiatics and others who have never known any higher level of subsistence.   From the purely biological standpoint, much of the animal husbandry that normally takes place is wasteful.   Unfortunately in time of war, and post-war (or inter-war) emergency, the biological point of view must predominate.   For many years after 1939 the specialised production of poultry and pig products was, in all European countries, either economically impossible or politically unjustifiable.   Such animal husbandry as managed to survive was incidental to other farming operations, and the birds and animals concerned have been in the main scavengers of what would otherwise have been waste products. The one exception to this generalisation is milk production. Even in war time this particular form of animal husbandry must be maintained, for child life depends on it; even for adults it is an economical source of protein in the ration. Hence milch cows get the highest priority in the allotment of limited cereal supplies for animal feeding.

In time of peace there is a secular tendency for the general standard of living to rise. This is reflected in a relative increase in the consumption of animal products, and a stationary or declining trend in the consumption per head of wheat, potatoes, and other cheap sources of energy. In the course of the last century the relative cheapness of cereal products imported from overseas, and the rising standard of living in the industrialised countries of Western Europe, have influenced the character of the agricultural activity that tends to prevail in their own countries. This trend may be illustrated from both British and Irish statistics.

In 1908 livestock and livestock products were 67 per cent of British agricultural output. In 1925 they were 71 per cent. In the case of the twenty-six county area in Ireland the percentage rose from 86 in 1926–27 to 89 in 1929–30.

The tendency to specialise more and more on livestock and livestock products is, for all European countries where soil and climate are suitable and market outlets available, a normal and healthy peace-time development. In the circumstances of the free economies characteristic of the nineteenth century the ultimate explanation may be sought in the changes of relative prices, which made it more profitable to expand agricultural production in one direction rather than another.

The late Thomas Barrington read a paper entitled "A Review of Irish Agricultural Prices" to the Statistical and Social Inquiry Society of Ireland on 6th May, 1926. Some of the data contained in that paper illustrate a secular trend of relative prices which is significant for Western European as well as Irish agriculture. Between 1873 and 1896 general prices fell from an index of 100 to an index of 55. Wheat fell to nearly the same extent—to an index of 57. Butter prices fell only to an index of 65, pork to an index of 68, store cattle 1–2 years to 91, and 2–3 years to 92, whereas egg prices actually rose to an index of 120.

Comparing 1896 with 1913, general prices rose from an index of 100 to an index of 139. Butter prices rose relatively less—to an index of 115. Store cattle 2–3 years rose only to 133, but pork prices rose to an index of 178, and store cattle 1–2 years to an index of 147. Eggs at 147 exceeded the general index also.

When the prices of 1913 are compared with those of 1925 it becomes obvious that the permanent secular trend had not fully asserted itself after the dislocations of the first World War. The general price index was 160 in 1925 (1913—100), but wheat was still abnormally dear (179). Soon, like Humpty Dumpty, it was destined to receive a great fall. The pork index was below the general index (152). So, too, were store cattle, 1–2 years, at 152. Butter at 173 was above the general index. So, too, were eggs at 176. If these calculations were continued into the 1930's they would indicate a reassertion of the secular trend. The general principle may be stated as follows. In times of general economic expansion and rising general prices, the prices of animal products rise relatively more than the prices of cereal products. In times of general economic depression and falling general prices the prices of animal products fall relatively less than the prices of cereal products.

As we shall see, Irish agriculture did react in an intelligible manner to the change in relative prices. The reaction was unnecessarily painful because of the unjust land system that prevailed almost up to the end of the nineteenth century. But even if the land system had been an ideal one, the final result, in terms of the relative emphasis on various agricultural objectives, would not have been essentially different.

In 1873 the twenty-six county area had 2,479,193 acres under corn, root and green crops, flax and fruit. In 1913 that acreage was only 1,697,706. There was a corresponding increase in "other land," which includes "grazed and barren mountain, turf bog, marsh, water, roads, etc." The area under pasture and hay remained much the same.

There is a widespread belief that more tillage, even if it means less pasture, is synonymous with more agricultural production. This is not necessarily the case. A change from a tillage to a pastoral economy may cause some diminution of total agricultural employment, but it does not necessarily diminish the aggregate of employment and production in the nation as a whole, and may even contribute to its increase. In our special circumstances the change to an intensive grass farming economy and the further development of intensive animal husbandry (as soon as world circumstances will make it possible), might well increase the volume of production and employment in the nation's agriculture. An increase in total agricultural output, associated with an increase in output per head of agricultural producers, would provide the economic foundation for an increase in commerce between country and town, and, therefore, in the standard of living of both urban and agricultural producers.

If a farm is highly specialised for e.g. milk production or poultry product production it might well provide work for from six to eight persons per 100 acres of crops and pasture. It will make little difference to total agricultural employment, and perhaps none at all to the employment actually given on such a farm, whether the farmer concerned cultivates portion of his land to ordinary arable crops or whether he cultivates only a high quality of grass and buys the tillage crops he needs for his cattle and poultry rations.

A hen will consume nearly a hundred-weight of cereal products in the year, and half of that will consist mainly of oats. Thus, 100 hens would consume 50 cwts. of oats in a year, the produce of two and a half acres of land. From the national point of view it makes no difference, so long as a man is profitably feeding a large flock of hens, whether he grows the oats for them himself or whether he buys the produce of his neighbour's tillage. Normally, small farmers *must* specialise in animal husbandry if they want to make any sort of tolerable living. And they *must* buy the bulk of the rations which they feed to their pigs and poultry. Hence their special dependence on imported feeding stuffs; but an important proportion of their requirements in this respect is normally obtainable from other Irish farms if not from their own.

Output per acre is said to be higher on small farms than on large. In fact, the smaller the farm the higher, as a general rule, is output per acre. But the smaller the farm the greater is the relative importance of "farmyard products," e.g. pigs and poultry, as distinct from "farm products," e.g. wheat and potatoes. As we have seen, the small farm which specialises in farmyard products must have access to raw materials from sources other than the farm itself. Total output per acre includes the output of farmyard as well as farm products. Since the former bulk so largely in the economy of the small farm its output per acre appears to be very high. It is necessary to bear this fact in mind in interpreting the relevant agricultural statistics.

More tillage can sometimes mean less production. Something of the kind seems to have happened in our agricultural experience in the years following the outbreak of the Economic War in 1932. The policy of the new Government was to "speed the plough" and promote the maximum degree of agricultural self-sufficiency. Prior to that date the natural tendency to specialise in animal husbandry had led to the production of important export surpluses of cattle, dairy products, eggs, poultry and pig products. Hardly any wheat was produced at home, and we imported also considerable quantities of maize and other feeding stuffs. We also imported significant amounts of relatively low quality foreign bacon to take the place of some of the high quality native product which we preferred to sell in export markets. The new agricultural policy took the form of a guaranteed price for wheat, much higher than the world price, and also aimed at producing most of the 100,000 tons of sugar we normally consumed. The effect on our export capacity was injurious; but in any case our exports were tending to dwindle in consequence of the penal duties confronting them in the British market. In the course of a very few years the pattern of our agricultural output was drastically changed. The total tillage was increased. In 1931 we had 1,426,090 acres of corn, root and green crops, as compared with 1,698,000 acres in 1913. In 1938 the acreage had increased to 1,567,000 from the level to which it had fallen in 1931. But the emphasis was no longer on animal husbandry as it had been in 1913 and 1931. In 1929 only one-tenth of our agricultural output took the form of cash crops. In 1938 this proportion had increased to one-sixth. More tillage, however, did not mean a greater volume of physical production. Here is an index of the physical volume of agricultural production calculated by Professor

Duncan, F.T.C.D., and published in a paper read to the Statistical and Social Inquiry Society of Ireland on 26th October, 1939 :—

TABLE I

Physical Volume of Agricultural Production (Index 1929 = 100)

	1926	1929	1931	1933	1936	1937	1938
Crops	104	100	91	103	130	124	120
Livestock and Live- stock Products ..	92	100	103	93	98	90	93
Total	94	100	101	95	103	95	98
Prices	101	100	81	62	72	78	82

The increase in crop production reached a maximum in 1936, but in view of the relatively greater weight that was still attached to our (declining) animal husbandry it only carried the index of *total* agricultural production (physical volume) to a level of 3 per cent in excess of the standard year. In the following two years crop production declined from this maximum. The general effect of the whole policy was that, while the pattern of our agricultural effort was changed, the physical volume of production *as a whole* fluctuated closely round about the level of the standard year and displayed a considerable degree of inelasticity. In fact, if we may regard the increase from 94 in 1926 to 101 in 1931 as a normal trend, the subsequent years were years of arrested progress with a long-term tendency to decline.

One aspect of the change was a decline in the proportion of the oat crop fed to livestock. In 1926–27 this was officially recorded as 68·75 per cent. In 1929–30 it was 73·2 per cent —a healthy and normal trend. In 1934–35 it was only 61·6 per cent. The total acreage under oats declined as the area under wheat increased. In 1931 we had 623,000 acres of oats, in 1938 only 570,000 acres. Oats is pre-eminently a forage crop closely related to the processes of animal husbandry. The decline in its production, and in the proportion of the crop used for animal feeding, was symptomatic of the decline in animal husbandry that was the converse of the new emphasis on cash-crop production.

The acreage under wheat increased from 21,000 in 1931 to a maximum of 255,000 during the Economic War. Even that high level has had to be more than doubled during the second World War, and yet we had to rely on external sources for a considerable proportion of our wheat supplies in those tragic years. Agricultural self-sufficiency has continued to elude us with regard to this crop, and is now no longer sought.

We were more successful with sugar beet. We had 5,000 acres of this in 1931. During the Economic War it was raised to 62,000. In 1943 an acreage of 83,000 was enough to provide us with a nearly normal ration of sugar.

Our policy in the 1930's with regard to both wheat and sugar has been defended on the ground that it enabled us to come through the second World War with a greater degree of comfort than would otherwise have been possible. Both may be regarded as measures of national insurance, and both were certainly expensive at the time, in terms of higher cost of living and indirect cost to the Exchequer.

Actually, the growing of wheat before 1939 as a cash crop, divorced from a profitable livestock economy, was destructive of the fertility of our soil, and probably impaired our capacity to provide ourselves with an adequate supply of native wheat during the actual war years. The sugar beet policy practised is more defensible in the light of after events, but a policy of large-scale storage of cheap imported sugar with a smaller acreage under beet at home might have been equally effective and certainly much cheaper.

Our agriculture is mainly an affair of animal product production. Even in the midst of the Economic War in 1935–36, when gross output amounted only to £42,553,000, livestock and livestock products accounted for £30,934,000 of this total. In 1942–43, in the middle of the second World War, when crop production had reached its maximum expansion, livestock and livestock products contributed £57,584,000 to a total gross output of £86,203,000.

The principal raw material of animal husbandry in our case is, always has been, and always will be, grass—in one or other of its forms, fresh or preserved. We have normally about 8,000,000 acres under pasture and 2,000,000 under hay in a total area of crops and pasture of about 11,500,000 acres. Even in 1851, when the area of ploughed land was at its maximum, 3,509,000 acres, more than two-thirds of our total agricultural area, was nevertheless in grass. Grass is, therefore, by all odds our most important crop, and the principal raw material of our animal husbandry.

Lately agricultural scientists have attempted to estimate the "total digestible nutrients" derived by animals from grass, and express the result in terms of a common unit which will facilitate comparison with the food units derived from ordinary tillage crops. The terms "starch equivalent," "protein equivalent," and "cereal equivalent" are commonly used in this connection. The present writer does not pretend to any expert scientific knowledge in these matters, but he has derived much information from farmers who take an intelligent interest in their job. On an average Irish pasture a two-year old bullock ought to put up half a hundredweight a month during the six months that the average pasture maintains its feeding value. That amounts to three hundredweight derived from grass alone. At the usual ratio of 4 lbs. cereal equivalent to 1 lb. live-weight of beef, it would take 1,344 lbs. of a cereal ration to give the same result. Incidentally, it would *not* give the same result, for the lack of succulence in the cereal ration would have to be supplemented in some way.

About half the "input" of food is required as a maintenance ration. In an open winter an average pasture will provide a maintenance ration even in the six winter months. Only when the ground is covered with frost and snow is it usual to supply hay to our out-wintered dry cattle. If then an average pasture will provide a maintenance ration for twelve months and a growth ration of three hundredweight live-weight in six of these months it follows that the total cereal equivalent yielded is three times 1,344 lbs., or 4,032 lbs.

Allowing two statute acres of average pasture to each large bovine animal, it looks as if the food units derived from grass are of the order of one ton per acre.

Dr. Henry Kennedy, who is an enthusiast as well as a scientific authority on these matters, estimates the average output as "somewhat under 1,000 lbs. starch equivalent per acre." He adds that Stapleton and Davies, in their book on "Ley Farming," have given grounds for believing that a young ley pasture, if properly utilised, will produce 4,032 lbs. of starch equivalent and 7·2 cwt. of protein equivalent per acre per year.

Anyhow, there is no doubt that even if our large area of pasture produces only half a ton per acre per annum of starch equivalent it is by far the principal contributor of raw material to our animal husbandry as a whole. There is equally no doubt, that by the application of scientific methods of intensive grass cultivation, this output could be doubled, and possibly even trebled or quadrupled, in the course of a very few years. This is not only the opinion of academic scientists but of practical farmers, who have proved it in their own experience and profited by the result.

Even our tillage operations are normally aimed at producing food for animals rather than cash crops for direct human consumption. Grass is of fundamental importance, but its feeding value falls off in the winter months, and pigs and poultry require a more concentrated ration than grass affords. It is not generally realised that even pigs and poultry can derive an important proportion of their ration, perhaps a fifth or so, direct from grass.

Normally, about 70 per cent of our oat crop and 40 per cent of our barley crop are fed to livestock. Normally, the whole of our root crop and over 70 per cent of our potato crop are similarly used. Beet pulp has also been available for this purpose to an increasing extent. The total of these, expressed in terms of cereal equivalent, represents the contribution of our own agriculture, apart from grass, to the supply of raw materials for animal husbandry.

Among imported raw materials maize is of chief importance. Since 1932 the import of maize meal has practically ceased. The grain has been imported and ground into meal over here. A certain amount of wheaten bye-products have also been regularly imported.

There is also an item referred to in the table below as "Home Processed Wheaten Bye-products." This doubtless includes some bye-products of home-grown wheat, but also no doubt some imported materials. As it was impossible to say in what proportion they were home-grown or imported, they are placed in a separate column. The data contained in the table below are adapted from p. 97 of the Majority Report on Agricultural Policy, issued by the Committee of Inquiry on Post-Emergency Agricultural Policy.

TABLE II

Raw materials for animal husbandry (in thousands of cereal tons).

Products of	1926	1932	1936	1939	1940	1943	1947	1948	1949
Domestic tillage									
Oats (1)	443	435	358	374	502	552	542	657	464
Barley (2)	72	53	61	37	69	94	43	50	78
Potatoes (3)	308	579	430	575	605	599	475	644	498
Turnips (4)	374	338	266	258	244	226	237	246	199
Mangles (5)	168	164	160	169	170	142	125	138	144
Beet Pulp (6)	6	11	46	30	48	53	35	45	47
Total (1) to (6)	1,371	1,580	1,321	1,443	1,638	1,666	1,457	1,780	1,430
Imports									
Maize (7)	323	561	217	408	289	Nil	76	225	290
Maize meal (8)	43	24	Nil	2	2	Nil	2	2	4
Wheaten by-products (9)	22	40	1	31	15	Nil	3	5	Nil
Total (7) to (9)	388	625	218	441	306	Nil	81	232	294
Home processed Wheaten by-products (10)	86	89	152	164	146	11	57	64	93
Total available supplies	1,845	2,294	1,691	2,047	2,090	1,677	1,595	2,076	1,817

In arriving at units of cereal equivalent it was assumed that the food value of oats, barley and maize were much the same, weight for weight. In the case of turnips and mangels the gross weight of the annual crop was divided by ten in order to arrive at the cereal equivalent. In the case of potatoes, the gross weight of the crop available for animal feed was divided by four.

In interpreting this table it must be constantly kept in mind that it refers only to a fraction of our grand total of raw materials for animal product production. It does not include the food units supplied by 8,000,000 acres of pasture and 2,000,000 acres of hay and silage. In 1913 we had just over 2,000,000 acres under hay. The yield was just over 4,500,000 tons. This has been officially calculated as equivalent to just over 1,000,000 starch tons in food value (Agricultural Statistics, 1847–1926, p. 11). Apparently, it takes about four tons of hay to yield one ton of what is called for short S.E. In 1913 we had a yield of 850,000 tons of wheat, oats, barley and rye, and the S.E. equivalent of this total is given as 531,000. Very roughly we may assume that eight units of cereal equivalent contain five units of S.E. In terms of cereal equivalent, then, 1,000,000 tons of S.E. derived from hay (in 1913) may be shown as 1,600,000 tons.

We have already seen that Dr. Kennedy estimates the average output of our 8,000,000 acres of good, bad and indifferent pasture, very conservatively, at 1,000 lbs. S.E. per acre. This is evidently the same as 1,600 lbs. of cereal equivalent. In 1913 we had nearly 8,500,000 acres of permanent pasture. Consequently, its output of food units in terms of cereal equivalent may be estimated at just over 6,000,000 tons.

It comes to this, then, that in 1913, in addition to the food units derived from our own tillage and from imported supplies, we had 6,000,000 tons from native pasture and 1,600,000 tons from native hay. When we come to the years following 1926, which are more significant for our present purpose, these totals will doubtless require some modification, *but the order of magnitude will remain the same,* in comparison with food units derived from tillage and imports.

Referring now more particularly to the latter it will be seen from the table that ''Total Available Supplies'' increased fom 1,845,000 cereal tons in 1926 to a maximum of 2,294,000 in round figures in 1932. During the "years which the locusts (of Economic War) have eaten" the total fell to 1,691,000 (in 1936), rose again to 2,090,000 in 1940, but fell again afterwards. The tendency to recovery was effectively checked by the circumstances resulting from the second World War. It will be observed that imported supplies practically disappeared after 1940, and our native tillage effort, much strained by the endeavour to feed the human population, was quite unable to compensate for the deficiency in animal feed. It will also be noted that in all the years under consideration domestic production contributed the lion's share of total available supplies. Even in 1931, when imported supplies were temptingly cheap and the import of maize nearly doubled, domestic production nevertheless contributed 60 per cent of the total in question.[3]

[3] See table on page 97 of Majority Report on Agricultural Policy by Post-Emergency Committee.

The decline of tillage in 1931 was represented as proof positive of agricultural ruin, but the ruin was to come later in some degree when tillage had been stimulated to display an unhealthy increase.

Among native "forage" crops oats plus barley, potatoes and roots contribute each about a third of the total.

Quantitatively the import of animal feed is relatively unimportant, but qualitatively it is of pivotal importance. The products of native tillage do not provide a balanced ration for livestock.   The cereals, potatoes and roots contribute mainly carbohydrate and are all weak in various degrees in the protein element.   Grass, hay, silage and skim milk (a bye-product of grass husbandry in our case) are the only animal foods of native origin which contain an adequate proportion of protein.   Consequently native tillage for the production of animal feed is and must be closely integrated with the import of those supplementary elements which native tillage cannot provide.   *Only to the extent that our agriculture is based on grass, fresh or preserved, can we hope to achieve agricultural self-sufficiency with regard to animal feed.*

There is a natural affinity between skim milk and potatoes. In combination they provide an almost ideally balanced ration for pigs or poultry.   Unfortunately they are so bulky that they must be supplemented by "concentrates" if optimum output is to be secured.   It is still more unfortunate that skim milk is only available in the summer when the old crop potatoes have all gone bad, and potatoes are only available in quantity when skim milk is scarce.   Consequently each of these valuable native raw materials is apt to be wasted when for any reason it is impossible to supplement them by concentrates of domestic or external origin.   Such waste regularly happened during the second World War.

Finally, it may be noted that the total area under hay did not vary significantly between 1913 and 1943.   The area under pasture was about 8,000,000 acres between 1929 and 1939.   Owing to the necessary increase of tillage it declined to 7,142,000 acres in 1943.   Consequently we may assume that in that year only 5,000,000 tons of cereal equivalent were available from that source for our livestock instead of just over 6,000,000 tons, as in 1913.

These results will have greater significance if set out in the form of a table.

48 IRISH AGRICULTURE IN TRANSITION

TABLETABLE III.

Cereal Equivalent (in thousands of cereal tons) available from

	1932	1936	1939	1943	1947	1948	1949
Pasture	6,000	6,000	6,000	5,000	5,100	5,200	5,600
Hay	1,700	1,570	1,480	1,510	1,600	1,600	1,600
Domestic tillage	1,580	1,321	1.443	1,666	1,457	1,780	1,430
Imports	625	218	441	Nil	81	232	294
Total	9,905	9,109	9,364	8,176	8,238	8,812	8,924

The post-1943 figures in both these tables have been calculated as far as possible in accordance with the principles on which the figures published in the official report have been calculated. (See page 29, paragraph 77, of the Majority Report on Agricultural Policy by the Committee on Post-Emergency Agricultural Policy for a description of the method.) No great accuracy is claimed for the figures themselves but the "order of magnitude" is almost certainly right. They do at least illustrate the relative magnitude of the products of domestic tillage, as raw materials for our animal husbandry, in comparison with imports, which are supplementary. The latter in their capacity as "missing components" have, nevertheless, an importance which is more than proportional to their relative quantity.

The overwhelming importance of grass and its derivatives, even in their present neglected and imperfect condition, is perhaps the chief significance of these tables.

CHAPTER V

SPEEDING THE PLOUGH

THE outbreak of the Economic War in July, 1932, obstructed the normal outlet for the final products of tillage as well as of grass husbandry. In 1933 there was a good crop of oats, and the price fell to 5/4 a cwt. At that price there would have been a big decrease in oat cultivation during the next few years, despite the contemporary reduction in the import of maize, because it was unprofitable to produce oats for sale at so low a price. The price of eggs, into which much of our oat crop is normally transformed, was also low in consequence of the impact of the Economic War. The Government first looked to the reduction in the imports of maize as providing a fresh outlet for home grown cereals, but this reduction could only expand the production of, and demand for, native oats, if the price of this raw material was such, in relation to the price of eggs and stall-fed beef, as would make it profitable for farmers specialising in oat production to produce it, and for other farmers specialising in animal husbandry to buy it as a raw material. At the prevailing price in 1933 of oats, eggs, and cattle, it was unprofitable to expand the production of any of these important products.

On the 1st June, 1933, we had 22½ million poultry of all classes and ages. About 10 millions of these were ordinary laying hens. A hen will consume about half a cwt. of oats per annum (if allowed to do so). So with a view to maintaining and increasing the production and price of oats it was necessary to lift the price of eggs. On the 1st May, 1933, a bounty of 2/- per 120 was provided on exported eggs, and that bounty was maintained at a level varying between 2/- and 4/- during the whole period of the Economic War. The price of oats averaged 7/7 in 1934 and did not fall below 6/7 in any of the later Economic War years. In spite of the increase in the area under wheat the area under oats showed only a moderate reduction. The decision to lift the price of eggs in this way was certainly a politic one. That it was also influenced by political considerations goes without saying. Poultry production bulks largely in small farm economy.

In 1932 the area under corn, root, and green crops, flax and fruit, was 1,424,000 acres. In 1938 it had expanded only to 1,567,000 acres, in spite of the " guaranteed price " which increased the wheat acreage by about 200,000 acres and the beet acreage by some 40,000 acres. Our tillage economy was no longer integrated with a profitable livestock economy. Such expansion as did take place was the result of artificial incentives which were very expensive both to consumers and taxpayers.

It was these considerations which induced me to write in 1934, in the form of an " Irish Bull " as follows :—

> " The ship of our tillage policy is ploughing the sand, and the plough which we seek to speed remains stranded in mid air."

Undoubtedly the long term trend of those disastrous years was towards diminished actual production as well as towards diminished capacity to produce. The increase in cash crop production did not compensate for the decrease in animal product production.

Sustained agricultural production depends on the maintenance of the fertility of the soil, and needs not only a suitable rotation of crops but a suitable supply of both farmyard and artificial manure, especially where tillage crops are concerned. The excrement of half starved cattle has little manurial value. Cattle which are house fed in the winter with a complete ration not only fatten more quickly but produce more valuable animal manure. This, when in due course returned to the soil, preserves and increases its fertility. Further developments in the production of high quality silage, from young specially cultivated grasses, may make it possible to dispense with the import of high protein meals and cakes for supplementing the locally available rations for fattening cattle. But in the years of which we are speaking, the high protein element of the winter ration came from imported meals and cakes—or else it was not available at all. Consequently another index of the state of our agriculture in those years will be found from the figures for the import of oil seed cake and meal.

TABLE IV.

Imports of oil seed cake and meal.

Year				Imports Tons
1926	..	..	..	..	46,815
1927	..	..	..	..	50,010
1928	..	..	..	..	47,595
1929	..	..	..	..	48,555
1930	..	..	..	..	49,215
1931	..	..	..	..	56,785
1932	..	..	..	..	48,085
1933	..	..	..	..	28,220
1934	..	..	..	..	32,760
1935	..	..	..	..	32,425
1936	..	..	..	..	21,445
1937	..	..	..	..	32,900
1938	..	..	..	..	27,900

This table was included at my suggestion in the Majority Report on Agricultural Policy, referred to above, and appears on page 31 of that publication.

These figures conceal variations in the proportions of different kinds of oil seed cake and meal imported. Linseed cake or meal is characteristically used in the winter fattening of cattle. Cotton seed cake or meal is normally used for providing the protein element in the winter ration of dairy cows. After 1932 there was a vigorous growth of the new industrialism, and a consequent expansion in urban population. More milk was needed for the towns, and this meant an increase of winter milk production on the part of those dairy farmers who specialise in selling liquid milk for human consumption. Only this limited class of dairy farmers is in the habit of feeding a complete ration to their winter milkers. In the Creamery districts the cows produce all their milk from summer grass, and subsist on hay and water in the winter time. Accordingly we note that the import of cotton seed cake and meal went up from 8,000 to 10,000 tons between 1933 and 1936 whereas linseed fell from 15,000 tons to 9,400. It was the winter feeders of beef cattle who, in particular, " took the knock ".

The use of artificial manures also greatly declined. In addition to lime the three important categories of these are the nitrogenous, the potassic, and the phosphatic. The use of the chief nitrogenous manures actually increased after 1934; the decline was most noticeable in the case of the phosphatic manures, and most of all in the case of basic slag, which is the form of phosphatic manures most appropriate to grass. The nitrogenous manures give quick results but

E

have no lasting effect on soil fertility, and are therefore likely to be applied when it is a question of snatching a quick cash profit from the cultivation of wheat or beet. The potash and phosphate manures take longer to act but have more permanent results.

In interpreting the Table given below it should be noted that Rock Phosphate is imported from Algeria and elsewhere and is turned into super-phosphate in our own artificial manure factories.   The super phosphate imported as such is therefore in competition with the product of Irish factories.   In the interests of perhaps 1,000 persons gainfully occupied in the latter their industry was " protected " to the detriment of the interests of more than 500,000 persons gainfully occupied in agriculture.   It should also be noted that one ton of rock phosphate is processed into nearly two tons of super-phosphate.

TABLE V.

Imports of rock phosphate and manufactured artificial manures.

	Phosphatic			Potassic	Nitro-genous	
	Rock Phos-phate	Basic Slag	Super-phos-phate	Kainit, etc.	Sodium Nitrate and Sulphate of Ammonia	Other fer-tilisers
	Thousand Tons					
1926 ..	56·7	31·3	41·7	8·0	17·3	11·5
1927 ..	70·9	38·4	40·5	9·5	17·4	13·8
1928 ..	60·6	30·2	38·9	12·9	17·6	14·2
1929 ..	93·3	34·9	44·5	13·4	24·4	24·8
1930 ..	94·9	38·7	42·4	13·0	22·2	14·5
1931 ..	63·6	28·6	31·9	12·2	19·2	12·5
1932 ..	60·0	10·1	37·1	6·5	31·1	7·5
1933 ..	48·8	3·6	10·5	—	23·5	13·2
1934 ..	58·0	—	11·4	—	17·6	25·8
1935 ..	63·5	7·6	15·0	12·1	26·7	3·4
1936 ..	72·2	15·1	8·2	9·6	30·7	2·7
1937 ..	87·4	16·6	8·7	11·0	27·3	—
1938 ..	80·3	21·8	5·9	9·0	33·4	—
1939 ..	88·9	9·6	9·1	8·9	30·9	23·1
1940 ..	73·6	20·2	15·4	*	47·4	20·3
1941 ..	6·7	Nil	2·0	Nil	1·0	1·0
1942 ..	Nil	Nil	*	Nil	·7	1·0
1943 ..	Nil	Nil	*	Nil	*	Nil
1944 ..	7·0	*		Nil	·5	*

* Quantities less than 1,000 tons.

From this Table it appears that in the peak year (1929)
some 266,000 tons of phosphatic manure in all were applied
to Irish Land; of this total about 180,000 tons was derived
from the import of 93,300 tons of rock phosphate. During
the Economic War years the application of these diminished
by about half.   This was one of the most disastrous of the
Irish farmers' financial economies in those wasted years.
Plenty of phosphatic manures were available but they felt
they could not afford to buy them.   During the years of
the second World War it became a physical impossibility to
acquire any worth while quantities of phosphatic or other
artificial manures at all.   Consequently, as compared with
the peak year—1929—, there is a deficiency of the order of
100,000 tons per annum on the average of the years 1931
to 1939.   The deficiency on the average of the years 1940
to 1945 seems to be of the order of 200,000 tons per annum.
The total deficiency with which we were faced after 1945
must therefore have been at least 2,000,000 tons on the
assumption that the rate of application of 1929 would not
have been excessive if consistently maintained in every year
since then.

   The data about phosphatic manures contained in Table V
can be expressed in terms of a common unit if we take 28%
of the weight of rock phosphate, 18% of the weight of basic
slag, and 16% of superphosphate as representing the P_2O_5
content.   Dr. Walsh of the Department of Agriculture has
kindly supplied me with the additional information which
enabled me to prepare Table Va and Diagram.

TABLE Va.

Application of phosphate in tons of P_2O_5.

Year	P_2O_5
1945	7920
1946	5310
1947	24,400
1948	36,760
1949	50,000
1950	51,752

   The significance of Diagram I, which thus covers the
whole period from 1926 to 1950, can now be appreciated.

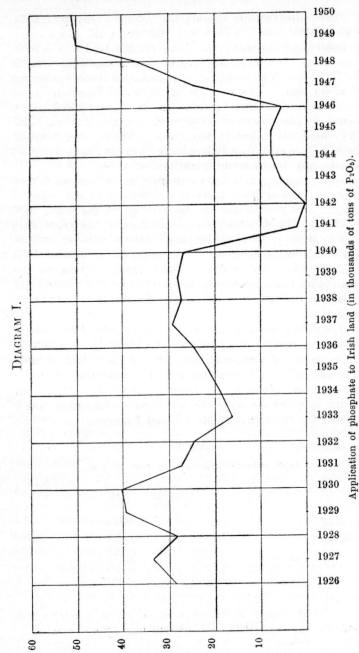

DIAGRAM I.

Application of phosphate to Irish land (in thousands of tons of P_2O_5).

The circumstances associated with the Economic War imposed on our Government the apparent necessity of practising a near-war economy. This involved a temporary revolution in our natural agricultural policy, distorting it away from the tendency to specialise in livestock and livestock product production. It has been held that our policy of encouraging wheat production in the 1930's made us better fitted to expand wheat production when the World War made it a painful necessity. This is so only to the extent that many farmers learnt the technique of wheat production for the first time, and that a more adequate supply of seed, machinery, and wheat processing equipment was available in 1939 than would otherwise have been the case.

In other respects the production of wheat in those inter-war years, without a solid foundation in a profitable live stock economy, produced a cumulative deterioration of soil fertility from which it will take years to recover. Consequently our soil was less fitted to grow wheat after 1939 because it had grown so much after 1932. If in the 1930's our cattle husbandry had been on a profitable basis, with plenty of winter fed beef cattle, and plenty of farmyard manure to grow the root crops which clean the land, we could have grown a reasonable amount of wheat without injury to the soil and perhaps with advantage to the national economy.

In fact our traditional policy of specialisation on animal husbandry, with reliance on grass, and tillage to supplement the winter deficiencies of grass, is not only the most profitable in time of peace and normal commercial relations with Great Britain, but is also the best insurance for the food supply of both countries in time of war. Such a policy preserves and enhances the fertility of the soil and makes it possible to switch over to wheat production in time of war, even if manures are not available in adequate quantity. It is legitimate in time of real war to draw on the accumulated reserves of fertile pasture land in order to grow wheat, but to do so for the sake of victory in a "phoney" Economic War is, perhaps, good politics but bad economics.

CHAPTER VI

Feed Costs and Animal Product Prices

AMERICAN writings about agriculture have familiarised readers with what they call the corn-hog ratio. In essence it is the relation between the price of maize and the price obtainable for the pigs fed with maize as the principal part of their ration. When maize is relatively cheap more of it is fed to pigs and less is sold as a cash crop, and of course vice versa in the opposite case. As every Irish farmer knows, the same phenomenon of price relationships influences all forms of animal husbandry in which cereal raw materials play an important part. To the extent that animal husbandry depends on grass the situation is different. Grass has no outlet except as a form of livestock feed. When cattle are dear the value of grass and hay rises, and it falls when cattle are cheap. The farmer concerned can do little or nothing about it.

On the other hand he can and does vary the quantity of his pig and poultry production in response to variations in the cost of cereal raw materials. To the extent that he supplements the rations of his beef or dairy cattle with cereal concentrates he is apt to diminish or abandon the use of the latter if the price relationship becomes unfavourable.

Adam Smith pointed out the economic significance of this price phenomenon in Chapter XI of the first Book of his *Wealth of Nations*. With the growth of civilisation the quantity of butchers' meat produced naturally in a country is diminished on account of the encroachment of cultivated land on the areas where cattle have hitherto lived on the natural grasses. Hence, as he goes on to explain, the price of meat must rise relatively to the price of corn till it gets so high that it is as profitable to employ fertile well-cultivated land in raising food for cattle as in raising corn for human consumption. Until cattle reach this relative price it is impossible that the greater part even of those lands which are capable of the highest cultivation can be completely cultivated. Cattle are a pivotal element in all forms of intensive arable husbandry. " The quantity of well cultivated land must be in proportion to the quantity of manure which the farm itself produces; and this again must be in proportion to the stock of cattle which are maintained on it. The land is manured, either by pasturing the cattle upon it, or by feeding them in the stable, and from thence carrying out their dung to it. But," he goes on, " unless the price of the cattle be sufficient to pay both the rent and profit of cultivated land, the farmer cannot afford to pasture them upon it; and he can still less afford to feed them in the stable." The crux of the matter, as Adam Smith saw, was that increase of stock and improvement of land must go hand in hand, and a favourable relationship between the price of corn and the price of cattle was a necessary condition of any such development. " It is with the produce of improved and cultivated land only that cattle can be fed in the stable. If the price of the cattle, therefore, is not sufficient to pay for the produce of improved and cultivated land, when they are allowed to pasture it, that price will be still less sufficient to pay for that produce, when it must be collected with a good deal of additional labour, and brought into the stable to them."

One of the first effects of the Economic War on our agriculture was that the winter feeding of beef cattle with any serious proportion of cereal concentrates became utterly uneconomic. " Stall feeding " was abandoned in 1933, and owing to the persistence of an unfavourable relation between the price of cereals and the price of fat cattle *even after the Economic War was ended in 1938* was not resumed until 1948–49. All through the 1932–1948 years there has been a chronic scarcity of the best quality of farmyard manure, owing to this cause, and this has had a cumulative effect on the deterioration of our soil. During most of this period we had to maintain a high proportion of tillage, and were forced by circumstances to practise a tillage economy which was not based on a profitable livestock economy.

Cattle cannot be profitably kept by the average farmer for the sake of their manure alone. And yet, unless adequate farmyard manure is available, agricultural production cannot expand and soil conditions must deteriorate. Hence the fundamental importance of such a relationship between corn prices and cattle prices as will facilitate a continuous improvement of both pasture and arable land.

Adam Smith illustrates this point by showing that the restricted market for cattle in Scotland before the Union (1707) kept cattle cheap in that country and delayed agricultural improvement. " Of all the commercial advantages, however, which Scotland has derived from the Union with England, this rise in the price of cattle is, perhaps, the greatest."

Similar considerations apply to the keeping of poultry and pigs. It will pay to keep twenty or thirty poultry and two or three pigs on almost any farm, because they will forage a living for themselves on scraps and unsaleable products of farmyard or kitchen. But there can be no systematic increase in the size of flocks and herds till the price of eggs and pigs, relative to the price of cereal raw materials, rises to such a level that it becomes profitable to feed them on the produce of cultivated land.

Broadly speaking we could probably manage to keep about 10 million poultry without any substantial proportion of their ration having to consist of cereal raw materials either native or imported. Actually about a hundred years ago that was the order of magnitude of our poultry population. It now tends to hover round about the 20 million level. The average poultry flock per agricultural holding is only about fifty birds. Although our poultry population has doubled in the last hundred years it is still far below the optimum. In fact there is no department of our agricultural activity which has expanded more in the last hundred years, and none in which there is even now greater room for expansion. Assuming the availability of adequate poultry feed, one factor in such expansion will be a suitable ratio between the price of feed and the price of eggs. As we shall see, that ratio was impaired by the first onset of the Economic War. It was afterwards restored by the bounty on egg exports. The onset of the World War impaired it again, but the ratio subsequently reasserted itself. During the war years the limiting factor in egg production was absolute scarcity of poultry feed.

In 1939 there were about 1,000,000 pigs on the 1st June, and about the same number between 1850 and 1870. That corresponds to an average of about $2\frac{1}{2}$ pigs per holding, and this implies no general large scale systematic pig production based on the use of cereal raw materials acquired from outside the farm.

There were also about 1,000,000 milch cows in 1939 just as there were in 1850. Since the requirements of the average family absorb the output of about 1½ cows the inference is that there has been no substantial development of the dairying industry if we consider the country as a whole.

In 1850 there were about 3,000,000 sheep in what is now " Eire " and there were about the same number in the 1930's. The number of horses and ponies has been about the same for about eighty years—not much over 400,000. Curiously enough the number of asses increased from 149,000 in 1851 to 247,000 in 1918 but had diminished again to 122,000 by 1947.

This sameness in our agriculture statistics is quite unique. Between 1923 and 1938 the cow population of New Zealand increased from 1,250,000 to 1,870,000. Similar increases in the number of cows have been registered in Denmark and elsewhere. The pig population of Northern Ireland increased from 236,000 in 1927 to a maximum of 627,000 in 1939, and the poultry population from 7,920,000 in 1926 to 16,600,000 in 1944. We had only 17,300,000 poultry in 1947.

In our case the only substantial and sustained increases of live stock population during the last hundred years have been in respect of poultry, and, most important of all, dry cattle two years old and upwards. In 1850 there were about 600,000 of them in our area. Between 1900 and 1930 the number hovered in the neighbourhood of 1,000,000 but it fell to 700,000 during the Economic War which hit the exporters of dry cattle very hard. In 1947 the number of cattle two years old and upwards was just short of 1,000,000, but " total cattle ", which reached a peak of about 4,250,000 in 1945 was in 1947 just short of 4,000,000.

The commercial and agricultural history of post-Union Scotland illustrates the favourable effect on agriculture of a suitable ratio between the prices of tillage products and those of livestock. The pre-1932 history of Irish Agriculture enables us to illustrate the favourable operation of the same phenomenon, and the post-1932 history affords an illustration of the disastrous results of an unfavourable price relationship.

It takes about 7 lbs. of cereal products to produce by stall feeding 1 lb. of beef dead weight. The principal raw material for beef production is, in our case, grass in one or other of its forms. But for winter beef production it is desirable to use some cereal products in the ration—and the extent to which this will be done depends on the price ratio. One effect of a persistently unfavourable price ratio is to drive the livestock industry back to an exclusively grass foundation in the form of grass, or hay unsupplemented by any winter feeding of cereal products. Actually it was so driven back, first of all by the Economic War and latterly by the World War, for oats has long been much too expensive a ration to feed to beef cattle at the relatively low price of the latter which prevailed up to recently.

Modern scientific investigation has proved that good silage made from young grass will provide an adequate substitute for the cereal content, and even for the protein element, in a full winter ration. The general adoption of this technique may enable us to expand as well as to cheapen the production of winter beef in the future, but it has not been sufficiently widely adopted to make any difference to the general position in the recent past.

The price of oats is typical of the price of the cereal products which have hitherto been used for winter beef production. In fact crushed oats are normally an important part of the cereal ration fed to stall-fed cattle in the winter. Hence a formula for the percentage relation between the price of oats and that of beef will be given if we multiply the quoted price of oats by 7, divide it by the quoted price of beef dead weight, and then multiply the result by 100. The formula is,

$$\frac{\text{Quoted price of feed} \times 7 \times 100}{\text{Quoted price of beef (dead weight)}}$$

or more simply,

$$\frac{\text{Q P F} \times 7 \times 100}{\text{Q P B (d. w.)}}$$

The price quoted is in each case a price per cwt.

The following Table represents the percentage which the cost of 7 cwt. of white oats bears to the value of 1 cwt. of beef, dead weight. The prices from which these calculations have been made are decennial average prices from 1881 to 1910, quinquennial average prices from 1911 to 1924, and annual average prices in 1925 and the following years. Prior to 1920 the prices were average prices for all Ireland. In subsequent years they refer only to the 26 county area.

TABLE VI.

Percentage ratio of feed cost to price of beef cattle dead weight.

Years	%	Years	%
1881–1890	67·8	1935	124·0
1891–1900	74·1	1936	126·1
1901–1910	71·8	1937	127·0
		1938	86·6
1911–1915	75·4	1939	93·8
1912–1916	79·4	1940	75·5
1913–1917	79·4	1941	108·7
		1942	101·5
1920–1924	77·4	1943	120
1925 ..	74·9	1944	104
1926 ..	75·3	1945	122
1927 ..	76·0	1946	120·1
1928 ..	77·3	1947	116·5
1929 ..	70·0	1948	75·6
1930 ..	60·4	1949	68·6
1931 ..	73·3		
1932 ..	88·5		
1933 ..	84·5		
1934 ..	139·5		

The first thing that strikes one in this Table is the stability of the ratio between 1891 and 1929—scarcely broken even by the first World War. The use of decennial and quinquennial average prices for the period before 1925 exaggerates the appearance of stability, but the annual fluctuations in the prices of oats and beef were on a modest scale. The maximum annual average price of oats in the period 1881–1890 was only 7½d. per cwt. above the average price for the decade, and the minimum annual price only 9¾d. per cwt. below the average. The margins were even closer between 1901 and 1910. The annual fluctuations in the price of beef were also close to the mean in each period. In fact this was a period of remarkably stable price relations annually as well as decennially.

The matter will become clearer if we take the individual years in which the price of oats was at a maximum in each decade or quinquennium and work out a ratio for those years. The same can be done for each year in which the price of oats was at a minimum.   Similarly in the case of beef we take the year of maximum and the year of minimum price in each period of five or ten years.   The following Table results :—

TABLE VII.

Percentage ratio of feed cost to beef prices in years of maximum and minimum oats and beef prices in each decade or quinquennium.

Max. Oats Price		Min. Oats Price		Max. Beef Price		Min. Beef Price	
Year	%	Year	%	Year	%	Year	%
1881	69·1	1887	68·1	1883	64·8	1887	68·1
1891	85·6	1895	62·0	1900	66·4	1898	71·6
1907	79·2	1903	67·2	1910	64·3	1906	78·1

One would expect the ratios to be highest in the years of maximum oats or minimum beef prices, and lowest in the opposite cases—and so in fact they are, but the difference is not very great.

The very low ratio of the decade 1881–1890 (67·8%) helped to bring about a big increase in the number of cattle two years old and upwards.   Between 1881 and 1913 the number of these increased from 812,000 to 937,000. Simultaneously the area under oats diminished from 947,000 acres to 703,000.   The relation between the price of cattle and that of oats certainly favoured the expansion of cattle, but it restricted the area under oats.   Superficially this might not appear to have improved matters, but the yield per acre from the oat crop went up as the acreage went down, from 14·3 cwt. in 1881, to 18·6 cwt. in 1913. In fact, according to official calculations, the produce in terms of starch tons of all corn, root, and green crops, which was 1,329,000 in 1881 increased to 1,441,000 in 1913, though in the meanwhile the area ploughed up for these crops diminished from 2,288,000 acres to 1,698,000.   To obtain a greater output of food units from a smaller area under tillage crops was a sign of greater agricultural efficiency.

On a further examination of the Table of ratios, in the light of other relevant agricultural statistics, it would appear that a ratio of between 70 and 80% is consistent with the profitable cultivation of a stable acreage of oats and the maintenance of a population of dry cattle, two years old and upwards, ranging between 900,000 and 1,100,000.

Coming to the Economic War period we notice that in 1932 the ratio was 88·5. In 1933 it fell to 84·5 becoming less unfavourable to the stall feeding of beef cattle—but only for the moment. In 1933 the annual average price of oats fell to 5/4 a cwt. By 1934 the price of oats had been raised to 7/7 and it remained very close to that level for the remainder of the Economic War years. Meanwhile the export price of dry cattle was exposed to the full rigours of the British Import duties, hence the fantastic price ratios of 1934 to 1937. At those ratios it was impossible to feed cattle with the cereal products of arable cultivation. So stall feeding in any serious sense simply disappeared during those years, and in fact was only lately resumed in 1948–49. In view of the annual average prices of oats and beef in 1934 it would have required 3d. worth of oats to produce 2d. worth of beef. With oats at 7/8 and beef at 51/9 dead weight as they were in 1937 it did not pay to feed oats to beef cattle. The ratio in that year was 127·0. In 1946 white oats fetched 19/11 and beef 116/6 per cwt. It did not pay then either for the ratio stood at 120·1. It is all a question of the ratio.

Diagram II is based on the data contained in Table VI.

As we have just seen it no longer paid during the Economic War to grow oats for cattle feed. In order to sustain the artificial price of oats after 1933 there was a rigorous restriction of the import of all similar agricultural raw materials especially maize. The import of the latter diminished catastrophically, as may be seen from Table II, page 45. Since most of the oats produced had to find an outlet in the production of animal products—especially eggs—the price of the latter had to be propped up, as we have already seen, in order to keep up the price of oats and prevent a big reduction in the poultry population. Only a small proportion of the total oat crop is consumed by non-agricultural horses or eaten as oatmeal by human beings. Hence the great bulk of the oat crop must be consumed by agricultural horses or used for further

DIAGRAM II.

per cent.

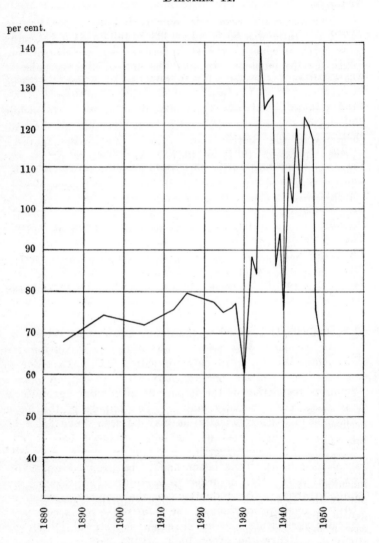

Ratio of feed cost to price of beef cattle.

agricultural production in some other way, and it is so used either on the farm producing it or on some other farm in the country. Hence if egg production had not been sustained the internal demand for oats would have diminished and it would have been impossible to maintain the artificial level to which the price had been raised in the home market. There would have been signs of over production. Even as it was the acreage under oats diminished to some extent during the Economic War. Those few farmers whose land was capable of growing wheat abandoned oats, more or less, in favour of wheat in order to profit by the guaranteed price for the latter. Oats has never been a " cash crop " with us, and it was impossible to guarantee a price for it on a basis similar to that of wheat.

In the following Table a series of percentage ratios of the cost of feed to the price of eggs is set out. In calculating the ratios the annual average prices of maize meal and white oats have been combined in a 50–50 proportion. For the recent war years there was no maize available and therefore no quotation of an annual average price of maize. The assumption was made that the average Irish hen lays 120 eggs in the year and consumes about 90 lbs. of a cereal ration in the form of whole grain or meal. The weight of 120 eggs is normally about 15 lb. Thus it would appear that it requires about 6 lb. of a cereal ration to produce 1 lb. weight of eggs. The formula for our percentage price ratio consequently becomes,

$$\frac{Q\ P\ F \times 6 \times 100}{Q\ P\ E \times 7\frac{1}{2}}$$

It is necessary to multiply the quoted price of eggs by 7½ because there are roughly 7½ " long hundreds " of eggs to the hundredweight.

The poultry population of Eire and Northern Ireland are shown in parallel column below, the latter as a "control" inasmuch as that area was not affected by conditions arising out of the Economic War. In both countries there was a gentle upward movement from 1926 to 1932, though in our case a peak was reached in 1930 from which there was a slight decline in the two following years. But whereas in our case there was a slow but not quite continuous decline

TABLE VIII.

Percentage ratio of feed cost to price of eggs.

| Year | % | Poultry Population (in millions) | |
		Eire	Northern Ireland
1926 ..	59·1	21·4	7·92
1927 ..	58·7	21·6	7·9
1928 ..	65·4	21·7	7·98
1929 ..	58·8	22·1	8·3
1930 ..	57·3	22·9	8·8
1931 ..	58·2	22·8	8·7
1932 ..	66·9	22·5	9·4
1933 ..	60·0	22·5	10·15
1934 ..	72	20·0	10·3
1935 ..	68·8	19·5	10·1
1936 ..	73·8	20·3	10·6
1937 ..	70·5	19·5	10·2
1938 ..	63·7	19·6	10·2
1939 ..	70·9	19·55	10·2
1940 ..	51·6	19·97	9·1
1941 ..		17·39	12·9
1942 ..		17·36	14·6
1943 ..		17·09	15·4
1944 ..		18·3	16·6
1945 ..		18·3	17·5
1946 ..	68·4	18·28	19·8
1947 ..	69·1	17·3	21·0
1948 ..	53·9	20·8	24·2
1949 ..	55·2	22·1	24·2

from 1933 till 1947, in the case of Northern Ireland a high level was maintained from 1933 till 1939, and the impact of the World War caused only a slight reduction in numbers. The upward movement was resumed in 1941 and the present poultry population of Northern Ireland now exceeds the level of ours.

It looks from the Table as if a ratio of less than 60% is favourable to an expansion of poultry population. During the Economic War the ratio became definitely less favourable in our case, and the tendency to increasing numbers was arrested and even reversed. Yet it still remained possible to turn grain products into eggs without financial loss, which, as we have seen, was no longer possible in the case of beef production. This was the result of the bounty on egg exports. Diagram III illustrates the percentage changes shown in Table VIII.

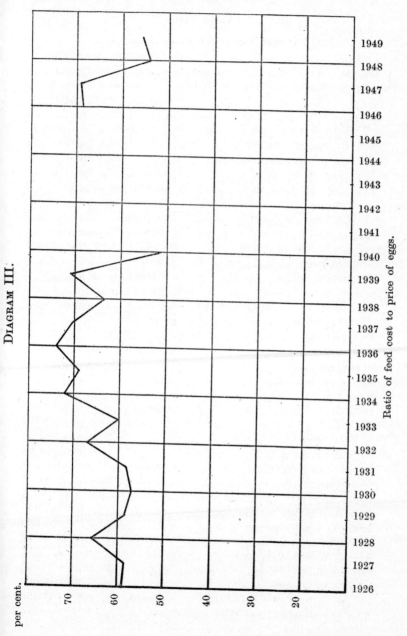

DIAGRAM III.

per cent.

Ratio of feed cost to price of eggs.

F

Yet the experience of Northern Ireland would seem to indicate that the ratio would have remained more favourable, and poultry population shown a substantial continued expansion, if there had been no Economic War and no bounty. Certainly if six of our Irish counties can maintain a poultry population of over 16 millions there seems to be no physical or geographical reason why the other twenty-six counties should not have a population of over 50 millions of poultry. The problem of bringing about this desirable result occupied the attention of both the British Government and the Government of what is now the Irish Republic in 1947 and 1948, with results that were satisfactory up till 1949-50. In 1951 the ratio again became unfavourable and poultry population again began to decline.

The formula for determining the percentage ratio of feed cost to the price of bacon pigs is derived from the annual average price of bacon pigs, live weight, and the annual average price of maize meal and bran combined in a 50-50 proportion. These are the principal elements in a complete cereal ration, but it must be remembered that in our case pigs derive an important part of their sustenance from unmarketable potatoes, and from skim milk when available. Potatoes by themselves are of little use, and skim milk, though ideal from the protein and mineral point of view, must have something solid to complete the ration. Potatoes would do but there is a lack of coincidence in time between the availability of skim milk and the availability of surplus potatoes. There is also a lack of coincidence in space. In the West of Ireland potatoes are relatively abundant, but milk of any kind is scarce. In the south-western creamery counties skim milk is plentiful in the summer, but there are hardly any surplus potatoes at any time of the year. Consequently in one area pig production depends directly on the availability of meals—usually maize meal—while in an area of surplus potatoes it is essential to be able to procure bran, or some other protein-rich feed constituent, if pig production is to be maintained or expanded. During the second World War these supplementary rations were virtually impossible to procure. Hence the sad decline in the volume of pig production.

In the period before 1932 these difficulties did not exist. The important factor then was the price ratio. As will be

seen from the Table below, there were indications of a
tendency to expand up to 1931 but, as usual with pigs, there
were fluctuations in both directions from year to year. In
the Economic War years pig production barely held its
ground. In the war years the pig population fell to less
than half the normal.

According to expert opinion it requires 4·17 lbs., on the
average, of a balanced cereal ration to produce one pound
of bacon pig, live weight, or 5·42 lbs. to produce one pound
dead weight. It will be noted that the pig is one of the
most economical transformers of cereal raw materials into
animal products, and that the percentage of dead weight
to live weight is very high. The formula for calulating the
ratios shown in the Table below is thus

$$\frac{Q\ P\ F \times 4 \times 100}{Q\ P\ B\ (1.w)}$$

Strictly speaking it should be 4·17 instead of 4 in the
numerator, but the significance of the Table is in the
variations from year to year, and these are in same direction
whether one multiplies by 4 or by 4·17.

It will be clear from this Table and from Diagram IV
that the price ratio was fairly well maintained during the
Economic War period. As will be seen later the effect of
the British Import Duties was neutralised by heavy subsidies
and bounties at the expense of the native consumer and taxpayer. Yet, in spite of our Government's obvious endeavours
to favour pig production, there was no expansion during the
Economic War years. A full analysis of the causes of this
failure is beyond the scope of this work. It should be noted
however, that, in Northern Ireland during the 1930's, there
was not only a free export market for pig products and
cheap raw materials, but also an admirable combination of
private enterprise and public regulation, to which must be
attributed the phenomenal increase in the pig population
shown in this Table.

The war time reduction in pig population that took place
in both areas was primarily due to the physical impossibility
of procuring an adequate supply of supplementary rations.

Again one might enquire—is there any physical or
geographical reason why we should not in normal times

TABLE IX.

*Percentage ratio of feed cost to price of bacon pigs
live weight.*

Year	%	Pig Population (000)	
		Eire	Northern Ireland
1926 ..	59·7	884·0	158·2
1927 ..	79·4	1,118·0	236·3
1928 ..	87·0	1,183·0	229·3
1929 ..	73·1	945·0	192·0
1930 ..	60·3	1,052·0	216·0
1931 ..	75·5	1,227·0	235·7
1932 ..	85·7	1,108·0	219·8
1933 ..	80·0	931·0	270·6
1934 ..	69·5	968·0	380·3
1935 ..	76·1	1,088·0	457·9
1936 ..	71·7	1,017·0	521·7
1937 ..	68·6	934·5	570·1
1938 ..	67·0	958·8	561·5
1939 ..	64·0	931·	627·1
1940 ..		1,049·	474·8
1941 ..		764·	350·6
1942 ..		519·	271·2
1943 ..		434·	257·3
1944 ..		381·	237·0
1945 ..		426·	249·
1946 ..	53·0	479·3	314·
1947 ..	61·0	457·0	334·
1948 ..	58·0	457·	335·
1949 ..	56·0	675·	458·

achieve a pig population of three or four millions in view
of the fact that our Northern fellow-countrymen were able
to maintain well over half a million in the last years of
peace?

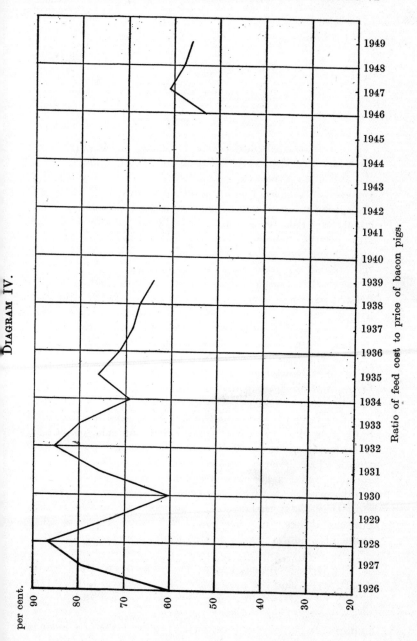

DIAGRAM IV.

CHAPTER VII

ÉIRE BOUNTIES AND BRITISH PENAL DUTIES

AS to the dispute about Ireland's liability for transferring the land purchase annuity payments to the British Treasury, it is only necessary to say that both Governments chose the worst possible means of settling it. The Economic War was an unmitigated disaster for both countries. But for it our *real* National Income might well have been 25 per cent more in 1939 than it actually was, and 25 per cent more to-day than it actually is. But for it, the volume of Irish agricultural exports to Britain would probably be at least twice as much as it is to-day, and her dollar and food austerity problems proportionately alleviated. The process of cutting off one's nose to spite one's face is sometimes good politics but always bad economics.

The United Kingdom fired the first shot, so to speak, by passing the Special Duties Act of July 13th, 1932. Many subsequent legislative and administrative salvoes were fired before the final settlement of April, 1938, which left some very important matters still unsettled.

It is difficult to assess the net effect of these combined operations on our agriculture. The amount of customs duty levied on a specific product was varied from time to time. The export bounties paid by our Government on specific products were also frequently varied. In some cases the bounties made available to the Irish producer or exporter more than counterbalanced the financial effect of the relevant customs duties, in other cases they were about equal in financial amount, while in still other cases they fell short of this level in varying degrees.

The British Special Import Duties were rightly so called. Apart from Empire preferences, an ordinary Import Duty is levied on all produce of a certain kind, and is the same regardless of the country of origin. Consequently all imported produce must bear the tax, and the incidence of it is on the consumer. But the Special Import Duties of these years were levied on specific products emanating from one country, and one country alone. Similar products coming from other countries, foreign or Imperial, were not liable to these particular taxes. Consequently the burden of these taxes fell almost exclusively not on the British consumer, but on the Irish producer. At all events that would have been the result if there had been no bounties. Since the bounties varied in amount in comparison with the customs duties, and were obviously designed to favour some export products more than others, the final effect on our agricultural economy was not the simple result of the British taxes alone, but of these as modified in their incidence by our Government's bounty policy.

In one of our official publications—Consolidated Trade and Shipping Reports (1935)—there is a convenient list of the British penal duties, showing how they were varied from time to time. The Act of July 15th, 1932, imposed a simple *ad valorem* duty of 20 per cent on all our agricultural exports of food products. On November 9th, 1932, the tax on live animals were raised to 40 per cent *ad valorem* and on other products to 30 per cent. On April 13th, 1933, instead of a percentage *ad valorem* tax, a specific duty varying from £1 5s. 0d. to £6 0s. 0d. per head, was imposed on cattle intended for food. On May 10th, 1933, the liability to duty was extended to all cattle, whether intended for food or not. Presumably, bulls now became liable to tax. The position remained substantially unchanged in this respect until February 19th, 1936, when the specific duties on the different categories of cattle were reduced. They henceforth ranged from £1 0s. 0d. to £4 5s. 0d. per head. There were other minor changes.

On page 33 of the Introduction to the official publication referred to above there is also a convenient list of the amounts paid in bounties on specific agricultural exports for each of the financial years 1932–3 to 1935–6. By applying an appropriate rate or rates of the British tax we can estimate the amount of money which the British probably collected from each of the products exported in each *calendar* year. This figure can then be compared with the amount of bounty shown to have been paid on the corresponding product in each *fiscal* year.

To the extent that the national bounty neutralised the British tax its burden was shifted from the producer of the "bountified" product to the general taxpayer. To the extent that the bounty failed to neutralise the British tax, certain aspects of our agricultural activity were penalised. In one case, butter, the amount paid by way of bounty (and subsidy) far exceeded the amount collected by the British by way of tax. The bounty policy discriminated heavily against our exports of dry cattle and in favour of our exports of butter, eggs and bacon. It is somewhat ironical that our cattle exports were in the war years our only important agricultural exports, eggs being a very poor second. Pig production and butter production were for some years insufficient for the home market.

Live cattle have always been the most important item in our total agricultural output. In 1929–30 cattle and calves were valued at £15,000,000 out of a total output of crops and livestock valued at £61,500,000. Even in the worst year of the Economic War—1933—the monetary receipts obtained by farmers for the sale of cattle and calves were one-third of their total monetary receipts from the sale of products at home and abroad.[1] Consequently a table showing bounty payments and tax receipts in respect of cattle is of special interest.

TABLE X.

Taxes and bounties on cattle exports, 1933–1936.

	Calendar Years.			
Estimated proceeds of U.K. tax on	1933 £	1934 £	1935 £	1936 £
Calves	72,500	47,500	27,500	16,000
Stores	804,000	897,000	1,284,000	1,245,000
Large Cattle	1,440,000	993,000	1,176,000	914,000
Total U.K. tax	£2,316,500	1,937,500	2,487,500	2,175,000
	Fiscal Years.			
	1933–34 £	1934–35 £	1935–36 £	1936–37 £
Total Eire bounties	729,000	530,000	297,000	Nil

[1] See my article in the Economic Journal of September, 1934, on *The purchasing power of Irish Free State farmers in 1933.*

It may be remarked that the British tax on cattle accounted for nearly half the total of the disputed moneys (about £5,000,000), and that the Éire bounties were a very small fraction of the total tax collected. The rate of duty was reduced in 1936, but the yield to the tax on store cattle was little diminished. The number of cattle exported as stores was tending to increase. The yield of the tax on large (including fat) cattle was temporarily inflated in 1935 by an efflux of cattle held back in 1934. Apart from that the export of fat cattle was already tending to diminish. By reason of causes which operated side by side with the Economic War, and continued to operate after the settlement of April, 1938, the export of fat cattle continued to dwindle, and for a time almost disappeared. The yield to the taxes on calves diminished after 1933, partly as a result of the adoption of a policy of calf slaughter.

Judging by the failure to pay a bounty big enough to neutralise the full effect of the British taxes on all grades of Irish cattle our Government were content to allow British policy to work its will in this department of our export economy. That this policy envisaged matters quite irrelevant to the annuity dispute soon became evident. In 1933 the British restricted by quota the number of Irish fat cattle that might be imported. They even restricted the number of stores that might be imported, but this was abandoned in 1934. They wanted our store cattle but did not want our fat cattle. The effect of these quota restrictions accentuated the already disastrous consequences of the penal duties on cattle prices. Cattle fell to less than 20/– a cwt. (live-weight), and export licences were bought and sold for £5 0s. 0d. each. The policy of discouraging the export of our cattle as fat, and encouraging their export as stores, was maintained long after the Economic War was concluded, and was abandoned only in the spring of 1948.

In 1934 the British initiated a policy of subsidising the price of cattle to the producer in the home market. That policy has been continued in various forms since then. The essence of it is that the seller of a fat beast obtains, nowadays from the Ministry of Food, a higher price than is covered by the final price paid by the consumer. The difference is paid by the Treasury, i.e. the taxpayer. The British did not want our cattle when sold in the British

market to profit by this producers' subsidy on the same
terms as home-reared and finished cattle. At the same time
they wanted an increasing number of Irish stores to finish
as English beef. If they had taken no further action the
price of Irish stores would have been "boosted" in sympathy
with the higher price now obtained by the producer of beef
cattle in Britain in consequence of the subsidy. Even amid
the complications of the Economic War all our exported dry
cattle would have profited by that higher price, for they
would all have been exported as stores however fat or lean
they were. So the British Government arranged a relatively
lower price for Irish cattle exported ready for slaughter
while at the same time it encouraged the export of Irish
cattle as stores by paying a price for British beef derived
from Irish stores, which was only some 5/– a cwt. less than
the price of home-reared British beef cattle. In 1939 and
subsequent war years the British Ministry of Food has been
the sole purchaser of our fat cattle exported for immediate
slaughter. Store cattle are exported by private traders and
bought by private persons for finishing. The degree of
price discrimination against Irish fat cattle has varied from
time to time, but in most years since 1939 it was true to say
that the price for Irish fat cattle, fixed by the British
Ministry for Food, was some 14/– a cwt. live-weight less
than the price that would have been paid for the same
animal if it had been British-born reared and finished. On
the other hand, the price fixed in respect of Irish stores
which had spent two months on a farm in Britain was only
5/– a cwt. less than the price for a similar home-reared
animal. The effect was that an animal in Ireland which
would become fit for slaughter in two months' time was worth
9/– a cwt. more if exported as a store than it would have
been if finished in Ireland and sold for immediate slaughter
to the British Ministry of Food. Hence the production of
really fat animals in Ireland (apart from Northern Ireland)
was persistently discouraged, and this has had an injurious
effect on our economy as a whole. It did not pay to feed
intensively in the winter time. An animal tied up for
stall feeding in the early winter, if not wanted for the home
market, would command only the Ministry of Food's price
when it came to be exported. Such an animal would have
had to be brought in as a store in the autumn, in com-

petition with British importers, who could look forward to a final price, 9/– a cwt., in excess of the price available in the case of the Irish feeder. So the Irish feeder just went out of the stall-feeding business, and only enough cattle were intensively fed in the winter months to supply the requirements of the home market. Sometimes even the home market was left short, and beef temporarily attained a high, almost famine, seasonal price, which came to an end when grass-fed cattle were available again. The bad effect of scarcity of high-class farmyard manure, in view of the war-time necessity of a larger tillage acreage, has already been indicated.

It should be emphasised that the really objectionable feature of British price discrimination in this matter, from our point of view, was that it disorganised the price margin that naturally tended to prevail as between different grades and ages of cattle in the home market. The home feeder simply could not compete for the highest class of Irish stores with the buyer for the export market. If he "stall-fed" at all he had to confine himself to secondary grades of store cattle—Kerry bullocks and the like, which are not in demand in the British market.

The producers of "forward stores" in demand in Britain profited by the favourable differential which British price policy reflected back on their cattle. Nevertheless, so serious has been the effect of the price dislocation during so many years, that quite probably our economy would now be in a sounder condition if the export price of store cattle had corresponded to the low price fixed for fat cattle exported instead of being regularly some 9/– a cwt. in excess of it.

There are larger aspects of this matter of price discrimination about which I wrote as follows in 1945 :—

"The principle of price discrimination has become in recent years a normal feature of British policy, and ours is not the only country which is affected by it. Accordingly, some remarks on its economic significance and implications will not be out of place.

"There are two principal methods by which an importing country may raise the price of home-grown food for the benefit of her own farmers. One is by placing a tariff on all competing imported products. In that case the consumer must pay a higher price with reference to the whole range of food products, whether home-grown or imported. The native farmer benefits by being able to command a higher price in the market thus protected. Obviously, of course, by this method the addition to the consumer's expenditure, in the case of a country like the United Kingdom, far exceeds the financial advantage conveyed to the nation's farmer. It is quite intelligible that public policy in the United Kingdom should avoid the use of this method.

"Another, and nowadays more usual, method is for the State to pay from public funds an addition to the price which the nation's farmers are able to command in the ordinary course of commerce. In that case imported agricultural products continue to come in and are bought at the 'world price.' The consumer pays no more in respect of any portion of his consumption than he would pay in a free market. The additional gain to the nation's farmers takes the form of a direct transfer from public funds. From the national point of view, this is the most economical way of conferring a special advantage on the national agriculture.

"Under war conditions the British Ministry of Food has a monopoly of the import demand for all imported food products. Consequently there is no such thing as a 'world price' in the ordinary peace-time significance of the term. We do not know whether or how long the British Ministry of Food will continue to exercise its monopolistic functions in the post-war era. Clearly, while it does continue to exercise them, and until other markets in other industrial countries are again available, it can exert a powerful economic influence on the whole economy not only of our country, but of all food exporting countries—most of them members of the British Commonwealth of Nations.

"There is reason to believe that New Zealand has found, during the recent war years, that her export prices have tended to be relatively lower than her import prices, and her economy has been financially embarrassed in consequence. This was recognised by the United Kingdom, and a substantial additional payment was made to the New Zealand Government to compensate for this disparity.

"In our case the export price for all our agricultural exports is definitely much less than the price plus subsidy obtained by the producers of similar products in the United Kingdom. The export price obtainable for our agricultural products is a principal element in the determination of agricultural incomes here, including the incomes of agricultural labourers. Agricultural wages here have risen in recent years but are less than the current level of wages in the United Kingdom by at least 20/- per week. Labour and capital move freely from our country to Great Britain —in which respect we differ from the other nations in the Commonwealth. Consequently prices for our agricultural exports lower than are in fact commanded by producers of exactly similar products in the United Kingdom, constitute a strong economic inducement to us to export agricultural labourers to Great Britain instead of agricultural products. We have, in fact, done so to an extent that now embarrasses our agricultural effort. This is a matter which concerns the United Kingdom as well as ourselves. We can see the reasonableness from a British point of view of the price discrimination policy followed in recent years. But its economic implications and repercussions have perhaps not been fully realised by those responsible for it. I am strongly of opinion that equal prices for equal qualities of produce sold in the United Kingdom is the policy which would best facilitate agricultural production in and export from our country. I recommend that a joint conference be held to see if the problem can be solved in a manner that will be compatible with the national interests of both countries."

The number of cattle exported as fat was as follows from 1931 to 1942 :—

TABLE XI.

No. of cattle exported as fat.
(000)

1931	..	247	1938	..	159	1945	..	17
1932	..	215	1939	..	103	1946	..	35
1933	..	230	1940	..	82	1947	..	111
1934	..	127	1941	..	*199	1948	..	66
1935	..	161	1942	..	82	1949	..	134
1936	..	157	1943	..	3·5	1950	..	179
1937	..	140	1944	..	20			

* In 1941 an outbreak of Foot and Mouth disease in Ireland diminished the export of "store" cattle. More cattle had to be exported for immediate slaughter.

The increase in the number of store cattle exported does not compensate for the decline shown above. Even if account is taken of the increase in the production and export of processed beef products, and of the increase in domestic consumption, it will be found that our total production of dry cattle has declined since 1931. There is no department of agricultural production for which our soil and climate are better suited. To double our output of cattle and calves in the next twenty years is both economically desirable and physically possible.

The British duty on eggs was 30%. Our export bounty varied from 1/7 to 4/– per 120 and was often changed. The following is an estimate of the joint financial result :—

TABLE XII.

Taxes and Bounties on egg exports, 1933–1936.

Estimated proceeds of	Calendar Years.		
	1933 £	1934 £	1935 £
U.K. tax	318,000	300,900	230,400
	Fiscal Years.		
	1933–34 £	1934–35 £	1935–6 £
Eire Bounties	280,000	487,000	237,000

Apparently in those three years we paid by way of bounty about £150,000 more than the British collected by way of tax. Our poultry product producers had no reason to complain of their treatment on this score.

When we come to consider the position of pigs and pig products we note first of all that in those years there was a considerable trade in the export of live pigs for processing in Britain and Northern Ireland. In 1936 there was an export of 100,000 live fat pigs to Britain and of 17,000 store pigs and " bonhams " to Northern Ireland. In 1942 this trade had almost completely disappeared and has lately been non-existent. Penal duties were imposed on the import of live pigs as well as of pig products and bounties were paid in respect of both. The general result is shown in the following Table.

TABLE XIII.

Taxes and Bounties on exports of pigs and pig products, 1933–1936.

	Calendar Years.			
Estimated proceeds of	1933 £	1934 £	1935 £	1936 £
U.K. tax on live pigs ..	124,000	148,000	171,000	170,000
„ „ pig products ..	365,000	655,000	747,000	814,000
Total Proceeds of tax ..	£489,000	803,000	918,000	984,000
	Fiscal Years.			
	1933–34 £	1934–35 £	1935–36 £	1936–37 £
Eire bounties on live pigs..	44,000	79,000	100,000	108,000
Eire bounties on pig products	284,000	567,000	474,000	526,000
Total bounties ..	£328,000	646,000	574,000	634,000

The bounties were thus a substantial proportion, but by no means the whole, of the amount collected in tax. However the native bacon curers had another and more obscure source of compensation. Before 1932 a substantial amount of cheap foreign bacon was imported, but one of the first actions of the new régime of that year was rigorously to exclude all such imports. The native curers were given a monopoly of the home market and they did not fail to profit by their opportunities. The regulation of the home market was entrusted to two Commissions set up by the State. One was called the Pigs Commission and the other the Bacon Commission. The objects of this policy were plausible and even praiseworthy, but for various reasons its history has been a lamentable one. By common consent the whole policy was drastically altered in 1945. The reorganisation of the business of pig processing is a task which still awaits accomplishment. In this connection we have probably much to learn from the example and achievement of the Government and people of Northern Ireland.

The bacon curing interests were adequately represented cn the Commissions referred to above. Since they had a monopoly of the domestic demand for pig products it was possible to follow a policy of maintaining high prices in the home market, and levying a contribution in respect of bacon sold therein, in order to build up a fund to subsidise export to Britain. So, in addition to the direct contributions from the Exchequer by way of bounty, the Irish consumer was an unwilling contributor. In combination these two sources probably neutralised the whole burden of the British tax.

The domestic consumption of bacon during those years declined as compared with the level of 1931 but the volume of bacon exported increased from 476,000 cwt. in 1935 to 546,000 cwt. in 1938.

In view of the fact that, for reasons already indicated, we were not, during the war years, able to produce enough pig products for ourselves, our efforts to maintain and expand the volume of exports in those years seem rather pathetic in retrospect. Our altruism at that time in insisting on paying part of the cost of the Englishman's breakfast has never been adequately recognised !

During the Economic War the position with regard to butter prices was the most anomalous of any, for bounty and (consumer) subsidy together far exceeded the amount of British tax collected.

The dairying industry was regulated by the Dairy Products Price Stabilisation Acts of 1932–1935 and many administrative orders made thereunder. A minimum price was fixed from time to time, which governed the price at which creamery, or so-called factory butter, might be sold, wholesale or retail, in the home market.   All through the Economic War period this internal price was much higher than the external price of similar butter.   In addition to the bounty paid direct by the exchequer, a subsidy was made available from the proceeds of a levy on domestic butter consumers.   The object of these regulations was to ensure a fixed minimum price to producers of creamery and factory butter regardless of the ultimate destination of the product emanating from any particular producing unit.

It was essential to the working of the scheme that there should be an import duty of at least an amount equivalent to the difference in price between Irish butter at home and in Great Britain. Otherwise cheap butter would have been imported in order to collect the bounty on re-export.

This particular fiscal device was first adopted in Australia where it became known as the Patterson scheme.   The principle of it has been widely adopted, in U.S.A. and elsewhere, during the inter-war period, and applied to many different products. In general it may be regarded as a means by which a product of which there is an export surplus can have its price raised above the world level in the home market, and raised with reference to the whole supply whether consumed at home or abroad.

As is well known the ordinary type of import duty will raise prices in the home market for domestic products only if there is a deficiency in their supply which must be met by imports. Such a duty cannot increase the price of any domestic product in respect of which there is an export surplus. In view of this it used to be considered impossible to " protect " any domestic product of which a surplus had to be exported. However the apparent necessities of the case, during the inter-war period, caused Governments here and elsewhere to develop the more complex procedure by which the price to the domestic producer, even of export surplus products, can be raised, partly at the expense of the domestic consumer and partly at that of the taxpayer.

Obviously the fixed price in the home market relates only to the proportion of output consumed at home. The proportion sold abroad must be sold at the prevalent external price. If the gap between these two prices is to be bridged for producers as a whole recourse must be had to the domestic consumer and/or the domestic taxpayer.

We are now in a position to set out the financial result of this policy in relation to the British taxes.

TABLE XIV.

Taxes and Bounties on butter exports, 1933–1936.

	Calendar Years.		
Estimated proceeds of British tax	1933 £ 399,000	1934 £ 417,000	1935 £ 525,000
	Fiscal Years.		
	1933–34 £ 1,449,000	1934–35 £ 2,045,000	1935–36 £ 1,205,000
Eire bounties and subsidies ..			

G

Thus the amount of the bounties and subsidies far exceeded the burden of the British tax. Our butter producers were getting in these years a much higher price for butter than they would have got if there had been no Economic War and no bounty-subsidy policy.

The favour extended to this section of our economy was in strong contrast to the treatment meted out to the feeders of store and beef cattle. Only trifling bounties were paid on exports of these, and the price, especially of beef cattle, was unduly depressed, not only by the British taxes, but by the British quota policy, during the Economic War period.

However, there is this to be said in favour of special treatment for the dairying industry. Our cows are in general " dual purpose " cows, and the surplus progeny of the relatively dense cow population, in the regions of specialised dairying, is an essential part of the raw material for producing store and beef cattle in other parts of the country. In the dairying districts (notably County Limerick) far more calves are born than can be reared and fed to maturity. Elsewhere farmers can feed to a further stage on the way to maturity far more young cattle than they find it convenient to produce as calves on their own farms. Consequently the dairying districts are, so to speak, the keystone in the arch of our agricultural economy as a whole.

In 1932 the dairying industry was said to be threatened with collapse. It was essential to prevent this from happening at almost any cost. The cost to taxpayers and consumers was certainly high.

It remains to enquire why the dairying industry, saved by and for the nation in the 1930's, was unable in the 1940's to provide the nation with as much butter as it would have liked, and still less able to produce and export a surplus of butter.

During the war years there took place a big increase in the domestic consumption of Irish butter, largely because other cheaper fats were unobtainable. There has also, owing to various causes, been a slight overall reduction in the total output of butter. The production of all butter (farmers' and creamery) was officially estimated at 1,218,000 cwt. for the crop year 1937–38, and at 1,077,153 cwt. for the calendar year 1945.

The reduction in the output of Creamery butter, the

distribution of which can be controlled, was more serious than the reduction of Farmers' butter which, in practice, has always enjoyed a free market. Limerick is the premier dairying, and therefore, creamery county. In 1936 there were 126,000 cows in Limerick, in 1938, 118,000, but in 1945, only 108,000. This reduction was partly the result of labour difficulties. A good deal of emigration to Great Britain seems to have depleted the labour force in Limerick and other dairying counties, and the farmers concerned have had to adopt a programme consistent with a smaller amount of man power. The number of dry cattle over two years old in Limerick, which in 1936 was 26,000, rose to 47,000 in 1945. As compared with butter prices in 1938, there had taken place by 1945 a big relative improvement in the price of store cattle. The natural response in Limerick, and other dairying counties, was to keep more dry cattle, of an older average age, and fewer cows.

The attractive price given in Great Britain and Northern Ireland by the Ministry of Food for whole milk for human consumption caused a great increase in the price of cows in those countries. There was a certain increase in the number of milch cows and springers exported from Eire during the war years. In fact if the export of such animals had not been controlled by licences distributed by our Department of Agriculture there would have been a devastating depletion of Irish herds. During most of these war years the Limerick farmer was getting the equivalent of 1/– a gallon for milk sent to the Creamery (including the value of skim milk returned). Those same cows, if functioning in the United Kingdom, would have produced milk for which the Ministry cf Food was prepared to pay a price of the order of 2/6 a gallon. The temptation to produce and sell cows for export rather than milk for local processing was obviously very great.

This is one of many examples of the way in which British price policies, operated with exclusive regard to British interests, can have a disintegrating effect on the Irish agricultural economy. In spite of political separation, the agricultural, and indeed the national, economies of the two countries remain by nature so closely interwoven that all artificial manipulations of price levels over there are bound to have repercussions over here. Since, however, the long term

economic interests of the two countries are complementary
rather than in conflict the practical conclusion is that there
should be almost continuous consultation between the
Governments concerned, and a disposition to study the effect
on the other country before any particular national price
policy is implemented.

Diagram V illustrates the incidence of taxes and bounties
respectively on the four agricultural exports considered
above.

DIAGRAM V.

Total U.K. tax and total Eire bounties on certain exports
between 1933 and 1937.

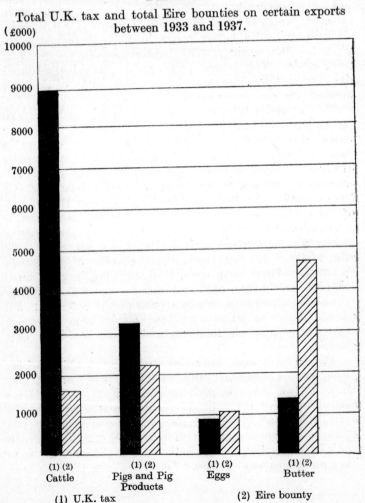

(£000)

(1) U.K. tax   (2) Eire bounty

CHAPTER VIII

The Capital Assets of Irish Agriculture in 1939

THE capital assets associated with our agriculture are a material factor in assessing its present position and future prospects. It is altogether desirable that a detailed farm survey should be undertaken officially and its results made available as soon as possible. We need to know, in detail, not only where man power and women power is locally in excess or locally deficient, but also what deficiencies of soil fertility, farm buildings, implements, machinery and equipment, are limiting factors in the increase of agricultural output. When all this is fully known there will remain a big question of agricultural policy and agricultural organisation. To what extent should individual farmers be expected to remove deficiencies in capital equipment by drawing on their own financial resources, or, alternatively, to what extent should capital be provided by drawing on the public purse or pledging the public credit? To the extent that the latter approach is preferred, there arises the further problem of reconciling the public with the private interest of those benefited. It is fatally easy to adopt policies of public expenditure which simply transfer wealth from one section of the community to another without adding anything to productive efficiency or the aggregate of the real national income. So long as our Government has to deal with a multitude of small farmers, very inadequately organised for purposes of commerce and processing and hardly at all for purposes of production on the farm, it is almost impossible to adopt any other policies. It will be suggested in the final chapter that the provision of public money for a large-scale rehabilitation of our agricultural set-up can only be economically desirable and politically justifiable if it is associated with a programme of reorganisation and integration which affects every aspect of our agricultural activities.

Using such data as were then available, the present writer attempted to assess the financial value of the various assets associated with our agriculture at the prices current in 1939. The results were made public in a paper read to the Statistical and Social Inquiry Society of Ireland on 27th February, 1942. No high degree of accuracy is claimed for many of the estimates embodied in this paper. But their order of magnitude is probably not far wrong, and the investigation as a whole does suggest that there are serious deficiencies in the capital equipment of our agriculture, and a consequent serious limitation of output per man and of total agricultural output.

In what follows I quote at length from that paper :—

The value of a farm from a strictly agricultural point of view is a capitalisation of the income which a purchaser, whose principal occupation is farming, might hope to make in virtue of his ownership as such. In making his valuation the purchaser considers the farm as a whole—land, buildings, fences, situation, water supply, etc., as well as rates and annuity charges, and does not consciously assign a specific value, positive or negative, to each item. All the elements of value which analysis may distinguish are, in fact, inseparable parts of a common whole. Nevertheless, for our purposes it is necessary to analyse and distinguish.

Our primary concern is to place a financial valuation on the various assets associated with Irish agriculture. One should note at the outset that a farm may be worth a certain amount from a strictly agricultural point of view, and worth considerably more by reason of its residential or situation amenities. Actually in 1935 there were 376,000 holdings divided between 374,000 occupiers, but there were (according to the 1936 Census) only 260,000 persons whose principal occupation was farming. (Banking Commission Report, p. 52, and Statistical Abstract, 1940, Table 32.) We are not concerned with the residential or amenity value of agricultural holdings, but only with their value from a strictly agricultural point of view.

As elements in the capital value of a farm one may distinguish land *per se*, accumulated fertility, fences and drains, farm buildings, etc. The unexhausted manurial content of land is apparently inseparable from the land itself. Nevertheless, a purchaser will give more for land which is "in good heart" than for land which has been exhausted by continual wheat-cropping without adequate manuring. Frequently farms are provided with stone-built farm buildings, which would cost thousands of pounds to produce at present costs of labour and material. To a prospective purchaser many of them may be quite superfluous, and all of them are worth only the expenditure he would be prepared to incur to provide the farm buildings appropriate to his farming programme if they were not already *in situ*. But the farm buildings actually available, whatever their original cost of production or hypothetical cost of reproduction, are worth at least that much to a prospective purchaser, and must be recognised as a separate item in estimating the total value of the capital assets of agriculture. The same general consideration applies to fences and drains. Not all land requires draining, but all fields require fencing, and fencing, whatever the material, costs money or labour both to make and to maintain. Consequently a certain part of the price paid for a farm must be regarded as the capital value to the purchaser of the fences and drains which he would have to provide if they were not already provided.

A further important element in the value of most farms is the value of the residential accommodation available. In other gainful occupations the business man may rent his dwelling-house, and need not necessarily own the real property associated with his enterprise. But the farmer who buys a farm must buy a house to live in as well as land and buildings to serve as the principal part of his productive capital. At least that is so in Ireland in the great majority of cases. The only exceptions are the beneficiaries of the Land Commission, who acquire both dwelling-house and productive capital without the necessity of any preliminary capital expenditure on their part. Economically, a dwelling-house is a form of consumer's capital, and should be clearly distinguished from a cow-house, a dairy or a hay-shed, which are typical forms of producers' capital. In most farm-houses the dairy is part and parcel of the dwelling-house, and in some the cows share, or used to share, the same accommodation with the human beings, providing incident-ally one of the cheapest known forms of central heating. Yet, however economically distinct, the burden of financing the purchase of a farm includes the cost of acquiring a dwelling for the farmer and his family as well as of acquiring other farm buildings. This is perhaps only one aspect of the well-known fact that farming is a life and not merely a means of livelihood. In practice, we must regard the capital value of dwelling accommodation as one of the capital assets associated with Irish agriculture, and therefore as an element in the price at which farms are bought and sold. It is an element in which the cost of production or reproduction is even more irrelevant than usual. Unless the farm-house has amenity or residential attractions for a prospective purchaser to whom agriculture is only a hobby, a farm-house of the most palatial character will be worth only the expenditure which a farmer-purchaser would be prepared to incur to provide himself with dwelling accommodation in its absence—unless it is capable of being broken up, dismantled, and sold piecemeal.

Portions of land in various conditions and degrees of natural and acquired fertility, in various conditions of fencing and draining, and in most cases associated with farm dwelling-houses and farm buildings, constitute what are known as agricultural holdings. Such holdings form the major part of the fixed capital associated with Irish agriculture, but by no means the whole of it. It is these units which change hands when farms are bought and sold; it is these which are capable of being mortgaged, and it is these which in the vast majority of cases are subject to Land Commission annuities. The amount of agricultural land held in fee-simple is still quite inconsiderable, though in theory all of it will be so held when the annuities, now a form of land tax, have completed the terms assigned to them in the various Land Purchase Acts.

Agricultural implements and machines form another part of the fixed capital of agriculture, in the economic sense. Such machinery and equipment might be distinguished on a functional basis into—(1) sources of power, e.g. tractors, stationary engines, and (2) machines for the application of power, e.g. ploughs, harrows, mowing machines, transport vehicles, cream separators. In this connection it should be noted that the horse is still the principal source of power on the farm, though for purposes of transport to and from market towns its place is taken to an increasing extent (apart from war conditions) by the motor lorry, usually owned by a merchant. Implements and machines are usually classed as "dead stock," while horses are included among "livestock." But functionally and economically the horse belongs to the same type of fixed capital asset as the tractor or other mechanical source of power. In estimating the extent to which agricultural hands are provided with labour-saving horse-power it will be convenient to consider horse-power in its literal as well as its derivative sense. Of course, in the special case of farmers who breed horses for sale, much of their stock of horses will represent the type of capital known as "intermediate products" or "goods in process," and to that limited extent horses should be classed with other forms of livestock.

Occasionally one comes across a farm which, while maintaining a general basis of mixed farming, has developed one aspect of agricultural production out of all proportion to all the other aspects. Such a farm would be one which specialised in tomato production, or in poultry and egg production, or in the production of high-grade milk for consumption as whole milk. In such a case it seems doubtful whether e.g. portable poultry houses should be classed as buildings or as machines or as equipment. Like buildings, they give shelter, but, unlike permanent buildings, they can be sold apart from the farm. Tomato houses are likely to be more permanent, and so should be treated as buildings. In any case, it does not greatly matter, since, from the economic point of view, all alike constitute part of the fixed capital appropriate to a particular agricultural speciality. In cases like these, where agriculture is highly specialised, the fixed capital appropriate to that type of farming, whether it be classed as buildings, machines or equipment, must be valued at least at production cost, less depreciation, and might well be worth its replacement or reproduction cost, which would doubtless be higher. In the few farms of this type which have come under my personal observation it will be noted that instrumental capital per person occupied is very much higher than the norm. Incidentally, employment per 100 acres and output per acre are also very much supernormal in such cases.

It will be convenient to lump together as instrumental capital all implements, machines and sources of power, whether animate or inanimate, and all equipment which can be sold apart from the farm.

Coming to livestock proper, we are immediately face to face with the fact that breeding stock, male and female, are by far the most important part of the fixed capital of most farms, if we ignore the value of land and farm buildings. Strictly speaking, we should distinguish a separate valuation for bulls and cows, rams and ewes, boars and sows, cocks, turkey cocks, drakes and ganders, but the statistical data are not adequate. Bulls and cows are, however, of quite outstanding importance. In the farms investigated by Mr. Murphy, of University College, Cork, cows valued at about £12 each represented 13·6 per cent of the total capital valuation (p. 9 of paper read on 25th May, 1939, to the Statistical Society), while farm buildings represented only 12·6 per cent. Bulls are also of major importance. In 1939 there were 24,809 bulls in Éire (Statistical Abstract, 1940, Table 62). If we value these at £40 each, they represent nearly a million pounds. Cows are undoubtedly the principal item in the livestock fixed capital of Irish agriculture. Their function is to transform grass and other raw materials into milk and calves, and these, both directly and indirectly, constitute the major elements in the output of our agriculture. I am not sure that they should not be regarded as part of the instrumental capital already considered. Part of the difficulty of definition in these matters arises from the fact that one category shades into another in a most annoying fashion. Be that as it may, the valuations that will be arrived at suggest that production per person occupied, as well as per acre, vary directly with the value of instrumental capital used. An increase in the number of cows properly housed and fed would contribute just as effectively to an increase in agricultural income as an increase in the number of machines used or the number of acres ploughed and put through a suitable rotation. "Other cattle" are in the main intermediate products of husbandry, e.g. goods in process of completion with a view to consumption at home or abroad. But it should be noted that some proportion of the annual crop of heifers is needed for replenishing, if not increasing, the existing herds of cows. The average working life of a cow is about nine years in this country, but only about four in England and

Wales (British Agriculture, Astor and Rountree, p. 257). Consequently about 130,000 heifers annually are needed for maintaining the existing number of cows. Statistics rightly distinguish the number of heifers in calf from the number of milch cows and other types of cattle.

When we come to consider sheep, pigs, and poultry it will prove impossible to make any distinction in our capital valuations between breeding stock and other kinds of stock. Indeed, even in the case of cattle, they will all be lumped together for purposes of capital valuation, but the distinction is one which should be borne in mind all the same.

As far as possible the capital valuations are given with reference to the 1st June, 1939, which was the last date for which adequate statistics were available "for the duration." At that time of year the tillage crops harvested in the previous season are likely to be approaching exhaustion. Barns and hay-sheds would be nearly empty, consequently it was unnecessary to include their contents in our capital valuation. If a valuation were made at the 1st of November, tillage crops in store might well come to a large sum—in one case under observation £1,053 from a 211 acre farm. But on the 1st of June a farmer, though he has not yet got the return, has already incurred much of the expense in payment for labour and other requisites. It seems difficult to put a precise valuation on the capital value of this short-term investment of capital and labour (owned or hired) between ploughing time and harvest, but it should be noted that some command of capital (or credit) is needed if the farmer is to wait for his harvest even if he does not employ hired labour.

With some diffidence, I am inclined to assign some £20,000,000 as the accrued cost of current tillage operations incurred by 1st June, 1939.

In assigning values to the various items in our capital account I have been greatly assisted by the investigations of Mr. Murphy, already referred to, and also by Appendix No. 7 of the Banking Commission Report. Mr. Murphy's valuations relate to the North Cork–Limerick border—a region which specialises in dairy farming—and were made on 1st May, 1937. The index number for livestock (based on 1911–13 = 100) was 102·1 in 1937 and 119·3 in 1939. Accordingly, I have raised Mr. Murphy's capital valuations of livestock by 1/6 in order to bring them into line with their probable value on 1st June, 1939. The valuations of machinery and farm buildings I have left unchanged.

Professor Duncan's valuation of stocks in Appendix No. 7 of the Banking Commission Report is based on 1926 prices, but current prices are calculated from a rather complicated index, and the results indicated for the years 1929 to 1936, inclusive. In trying to establish the 1939 valuation I have not been able to follow Professor Duncan's procedure, but I noted the numbers of the various categories of livestock for 1929 and 1939, respectively, the values calculated by Professor Duncan for 1929, and then, in most cases, expressed the 1939 value as a change in proportion to the numerical change in the stock in question. In the case of cattle, Professor Duncan's valuation was given for cattle as a whole. Between 1929 and 1939 important changes took place in the numbers of different categories of cattle. In arriving at the 1939 figure I added 4,000 (more) bulls at £40 per head, 37,000 (more) cows at £15 per head, 52,000 (more) cattle 1–2 years old at £10 per head, 16,000 (more) calves at £4 per head, and deducted 188,000 (less) cattle 2 years old and over at £16 per head. Similarly, in the case of sheep, I deducted from the 1929 figure 124,000 (less) breeding sheep at £3 per head, and 205,000 (less) store sheep and lambs at £1 10s. 0d. per head. The prices per head were obtained from the prices shown in the Irish Trade Journal for June, 1939. I don't know if the procedure is in accordance with the best statistical principles, but the final result should give a sufficiently close approximation to 1939 values in terms of 1926 prices. It remains to note that the index number for livestock prices in 1926 was *147·3*, in 1929, *139·4*, and in 1939, 119·3. Accordingly the figures shown have been expressed in terms of 1939 prices by reducing them in the ratio of *147·3* to *119·3*.

This Table ignores the State's financial interest in Irish land ownership, which may be taken to be the capitalised value of the annuities then payable.

The total of 466 million pounds arrived at is strikingly large, but, though some of the items may be questioned, I believe it errs on the side of underestimation. At 1941 prices it would be much higher and probably more than twice as high at 1951 prices.

TABLE XV.

Capital Valuation of Assets Associated with Agriculture in Eire as at 1st June, 1939.

					£ millions
(a) Real property capital :—					
Land per se at £10 per acre	..	..	..	120
Fences and drains at £5 per acre ..	..	..	60
Farm-buildings at £200 per holding	..	..	75
Dwelling accommodation at £300 per holding	..	113
Total real property value	..	..	368
(b) Instrumental capital :—					
Horses, machines, implements, and equipment at £2 per acre ..	..	..	..	..	24
Specialised equipment (incalculable)	..	..	x
(c) Live stock capital (less horses, mules, jennets and asses) ..	54
(d) Short-term capital :—					
Costs of seasonal tillage operations incurred by 1st June, 1939 ..	..	..	..	..	20
Total a + b + c + d	..	..	466 +x

Mr. Murphy's valuation of land as on 1st May, 1937, in the North Cork–Limerick border doubtless includes fences and drains, and works out at rather more than £13 per acre, if we ignore the value of 123 acres of waste land.   In Volume II of the Memoranda of Evidence of the Banking Commission on page 1163 it is stated that "roads and fences and so on will cost £104 8s." on a (new) holding of 20 to 22 acres provided by the Land Commission, that is, about £5 per acre.   It does not seem wrong to assign a similar capital value to fences and drains in our 12 million acres of agricultural land as a whole.   If they were not there some person or persons would have to incur the cost of putting them there.   Whether £15 per acre for land fenced and drained or £10 per acre for "bare" land (doubtless an abstraction) is a fair valuation for 1939 leaves room for some difference of opinion.   The average value of our 12 million acres is probably below the average value of the 7,244 acres investigated by Mr. Murphy, but the price of land, as well as of other things, was higher in 1939 than in 1937.

Mr. Murphy's valuation of farm buildings works out very close to £200 per farm, and the average size of farm investigated by him was 74 acres.   On the other hand, the proportion of tillage in these farms was only 6 per cent as against 12 per cent for the whole country in 1937, and the need for farm buildings consequently less.   It does not seem unreasonable to value at £200 per holding the farm buildings needed and actually used in the country as a whole. The Land Commission spends £357 10s. per holding of 20–22 acres in providing buildings, which doubtless include a dwelling-house (*ibid.*, page 1163). Such new holdings are by no means liberally provided with farm buildings and "out-offices." In my own 20-acre farm the Insurance Company valued the farm buildings actually in use at £500 for fire insurance purposes. In a neighbouring 211 acre farm, farm buildings are valued at £3,390, and all are effectively used. In normal times there is no direction in which the capital used in agriculture could be more profitably expanded than in the provision of more and better equipped housing for livestock. Warm housing for hens and pigs would to some extent replace the Indian meal ration, which cannot now be obtained. A hay-shed is a great convenience and a concrete silo (obtainable in 1941 for £15 15s.) is invaluable on any farm. If ever peace returns it should be a principal object of public policy to encourage the investment of at least another £25 million in this way in the course of the next five or ten years.

In view of the fact that the Land Commission spends nearly £400 in providing 20-acre "allottees" with a home and farm buildings, it does not seem unreasonable to suppose that the average farmer would require a £300 dwelling-house, apart from the value of farm buildings. The average farmer is, of course, a 30-acre farmer.

Instrumental capital at £2 per acre is based on Mr. Murphy's figures, with some slight upward adjustments of the value of horses, justified by the 1939 level of prices. In a neighbouring 630 acre farm horses and machinery are valued at £1,104, which is not far from a £2 per acre standard. It is a particularly large and well-equipped farm, and the average 30 acre farm, with horses and machinery worth only £60, would be poorly equipped by comparison. A figure of £2 per acre represents the actual measure, but by no means the desirable limit, of expenditure on instrumental equipment, and this, too, is one of the directions in which the investment of capital might well be considerably expanded.

The item livestock capital is more or less self-explanatory. The valuations at 1926 prices arrived at for 1939 were scaled downwards in the ratio of 147·3 to 119·3. See Table XVI.

TABLE XVI.*

Value of Instrumental Capital for Farms of different sizes.

Size of Farms (acres)	No. of Farms	Total Area (acres)	No. of labour units	Value of Instrumental Capital	Value per labour unit	Value per acre	Value of Farm Buildings	Value of Farm Buildings per labour unit	Value of instrumental Capital and Farm Buildings per labour unit
				£	£ s. d.	£ s. d.	£	£ s. d.	£ s. d.
Under 20 ..	5	75	7·62	220	28 17 7	2 18 8	292	38 6 5	67 4 0
20–39·9 ..	18	543	36·13	1,506	41 13 7	2 15 5	1,755	48 11 5	90 5 0
40–59·9 ..	23	1,150	53·63	2,233	41 12 9	1 18 10	3,498	65 4 6	106 17 3
60–99·9 ..	28	2,027	83·47	4,112	49 5 0	2 0 7	5,620	67 6 8	116 11 8
100–149·9 ..	14	1,685	48·33	2,236	46 5 0	1 6 8	4,071	84 4 4	130 9 4
150	10	1,764	38·31	2,348	61 5 10	1 6 8	4,240	110 13 7	171 19 5
TOTAL ..	98	7,244	267·49	12,655			19,476		

* This Table reproduces certain data which are contained in Tables I, VII, and X of Mr. Murphy's paper (cf. p. 92 above).

The value of instrumental capital is only £28 17s. 7d. per person occupied on farms less than 20 acres in size, is nearly £42 on farms between 20 and 60 acres, nearly £50 on farms between 60 and 100 acres, drops to £46 on farms 100 to 15 acres, and rises to £61 on farms 150 acres. On the other hand, if the value of farm buildings is combined with the value of instrumental capital, the increase in value per unit of labour is quite regular.

The value of instrumental capital per acre used decreases almost regularly as the size of farm increases. The burden of owning and maintaining instrumental capital is naturally much heavier per acre on a small than on a large farm. Obviously, too, a 100 acre farm with instrumental capital worth £1 6s. 8d. per acre is likely to be equipped with a greater variety of labour-saving machines than a 20 acre farm, in which the value of instrumental capital is £2 18s. 8d. per acre used. This comes out clearly in the column showing value of instrumental capital per person occupied. Its ultimate significance will be seen in the next Table, where the amount available per unit of labour increases with the size of farm, and therefore with the "capitalisation" per person occupied.

This Table indicates also the desirability of a suitable mixture of farms of various sizes in all regions of the country. The large farmer can afford to own modern appliances, and is usually willing to let his small-farm neighbours have the use of them in return for labour or money. I do not see how it can be "economic" for a 20-acre farmer to own even a horse (unless he is also a road worker). My own limited experience would indicate that a farm of that size is more appropriate to an ass than a horse. Speaking quite generally, a farm of that size, even if owned by a person of Senatorial rank, might be said to entitle to asinine rather than equestrian status!

Table XVII is simply a reproduction of column 5 in Table IX of Mr. Murphy's paper. His figures relate to the period 1st May, 1937, to 30th April, 1938, and have been scaled up in my Table by one-sixth to correspond to the 1939 level of prices. Even at that they are absurdly low. A neighbour of mine, who farms 630 acres, informs me that

TABLE XVII.

Amount Available per Labour Unit (from Table IX of Mr. Murphy's paper.)

Size of farm (acres)			Amount Available (raised by $1/_6$)
			£
Under 20	..	..	74·62
20 – 39·9	..	..	65·43
40 – 59·9	..	..	73·15
60 – 99·9	..	..	86·87
100 – 149·9	..	..	99·16
150	..	..	107·01

his net output per person occupied was in 1940 £215.[1] In his case non-specialised instrumental capital amounted to £48 per person occupied or £1 15s. 0d. per acre used. Specialised capital amounted to £156 per person occupied, and the high level of nett output is associated with the use of instrumental capital in both its forms.

TABLE XVIII.

Number of Labour Units per 100 acres (from Table VIII of Mr. Murphy's paper.)

Size of farm (acres)			Labour units per 100 acres
Under 20	..	..	10·16
20 – 39·9	..	..	6·65
40 – 59·9	..	..	4·66
60 – 99·9	..	..	4·12
100 – 149·9	..	..	2·87
150	..	..	2·17

Table XVIII is a reproduction of column 4 of Table VIII in Mr. Murphy's paper. The number of labour units diminishes, as we might expect, with the increase in the size of farms. If we had more information about large farms

[1] Mr. Murphy's "amount available per labour unit" is based on "that portion of total output which remained after expenses other than labour costs had been met." It is close to but not strictly the same as "net output per labour unit."

which are well managed and fully equipped, especially those in which some agricultural speciality is highly developed, we might find that the number of labour units per 100 acres compared very favourably with the number occupied (or half-occupied) on small farms. One neighbour, who specialises in tomato-growing and has invested £3,600 in tomato houses, employs 3·65 persons per 100 acres. Another neighbour, who specialises in poultry, and has invested £1,775 in poultry houses and appliances, employs as many as 6·63 persons per 100 acres on a farm of 211 acres.

In this connection it should be noted that in England employment (including family labour) is 3·08 on farms 20 to 50 acres, 2·99 on farms 50 to 100 acres, and 2·83 on farms 100 to 150 acres, according to the Agricultural Output of England and Wales, 1925, p. 105.

In conclusion, it should be remembered that the gross output of our agriculture has scarcely exceeded an average of £5 per acre in the decade and a half before 1940. On well-managed, fully-equipped farms a gross output of £15 to £20 per acre is not only possible but actual on farms of all sizes though actual in far too few cases. It should be public policy to promote the increase of agricultural output to an average of at least £10 an acre, at pre-1939 prices, on farms of all sizes, and to further the intelligent use of additional capital investment as a *sine qua non* of such a policy. A neighbour to whom I showed a preliminary draft of this paper wrote as follows :—"I have put a good deal of capital into this place since I started farming, and from records I have kept consider that the increase of capital has had a definite influence on the output per acre of the farm. There can, I think, be no doubt that Irish farmers can and should use a great deal more capital than they do at present. Agricultural output would be increased and costs of production lowered. But I do think that we need a change of outlook among farmers, as well as more and better agricultural education. At present many farmers in this country would not know how to use additional capital to the best advantage; the general idea would be to buy extra land or buy cattle and take land to feed them on, instead of putting the money into their farms."

The capital assets associated with the agriculture of Éire have been valued in this paper at £466 millions plus an unknown quantity representing the value of the specialised instrumental capital used by a number of our more progressive farmers, which is all too small. In the main these capital assets are owned by operating farmers, and the aggregate of agricultural indebtedness is a small proportion of the total value of agricultural assets. Only £12·59 millions was owed by farmers to the joint stock banks in January, 1937, whereas the banks owed farmers £35·61 millions on Deposit Receipt (Banking Commission Report, p. 206). Merchants are probably a more important source of short-term credit to Irish farmers than the banks. In addition, farms are doubtless mortgaged in a number of cases to private persons and institutions, and burdened with settlements in favour of members of the family who could not otherwise be provided for.

The custom of providing a dowry for a daughter on her marriage in the form of liquid cash is prevalent in many parts of the country. The cash has probably been accumulating for a generation as a Bank Deposit.

Such deposits pass from hand to hand from one family and generation to another, and are never spent if it can be avoided. The typical Irish farmer has more confidence in the banking system than he has in the possibility of expanding his agricultural income by the wise use of his own or borrowed capital. One suspects that there are many cases in which "surplus" daughters could be better provided for at home if taught the up-to-date management of poultry (or even pigs) and provided with the modest cost of the specialised equipment needed, than by the transfer of a Deposit Receipt for a few hundred pounds. An average poultry population of 50 per holding and pig population of $2\frac{1}{2}$ per holding is a national disgrace. But a revolution in our social customs and national outlook may be necessary before we learn the degree of national self-reliance which would be displayed if Irish farmers were prepared to use their own and borrowed capital in the expansion of their industry in those directions in which its expansion would be most easy for them, and most profitable for the country as well as for them.

EPILOGUE.

I have written this epilogue with a heavy heart.   One of my principal informants died with tragic suddenness a few days after he had furnished me with some of the most valuable data included in this paper.   Major Barrow, of Milestown, Castlebellingham, was an Englishman, and his widow is a member of an old and well-known County Louth family.   In 1923 the family mansion was burnt, this being the type of contribution to the New Order that was then fashionable.   Returning good for evil, Major Barrow and his family had their home rebuilt, and proceeded to develop a specialised poultry and egg-production business in conjunction with the cultivation of their 211-acre farm as a mixed dairy and tillage farm.   By farming on these lines they managed to find useful and remunerative employment for 14 persons, which is a very high proportion of employment per 100 acres.   If others had been encouraged to make similar use of the larger holdings, and had done so in a significant number of cases, the cry for "dividing up the land" would have had no economic pretext, and the absurd class antagonism between small farmers and large might have been avoided.   Political freedom has hitherto been productive of opportunities for creating and exploiting such class antagonisms, and only the consciousness of common peril has been able to create a temporary and precarious sense of social solidarity.   Major Barrow, by his efforts and example, was making a valuable contribution to a sense of social solidarity that would enrich our national life materially and spiritually at all times, and the premature death of this Englishman, who was an Irish citizen by adoption, is a national loss which we can ill afford.

My own personal debt to Major Barrow is very great. If I have any knowledge or wisdom about Irish agricultural matters I owe much of it to my contact with him.   He was always most willing to place me, and through me the Statistical Society, in possession of any records or information acquired through his farming experience or otherwise.   On the Society's behalf as well as on my own, I salute his memory with grateful homage.

PART II
CONTEMPORARY INFLUENCES AND TRENDS

CHAPTER IX

THE NEW ATTITUDE TO GRASS

TWENTY years ago the late Mr. Hogan, Minister for Agriculture in Mr. Cosgrave's Government, was being referred to derisively by his political opponents as "the Minister for grass." Grass at that time was regarded by many sections of Irish people as a kind of weed, which would grow anyhow, and was only less obnoxious than other weeds because it would feed cattle, but for this very reason was obnoxious in other ways because it was a substitute for industry in the feeding of cattle. There is now a more general appreciation of the fact that there is *grass* and *grass*, that there are a dozen or a score of different types of grass, and that the most appropriate mixtures of the best types of grass,—and clovers—will only grow and go on growing if industry is mingled with intelligence in a programme of scientific farming and stock management.

Grass is now coming to be regarded as the brightest jewel in the crown of the Emerald Isle. Tillage is now coming to be regarded only incidentally as the direct method of obtaining food for human consumption, but essentially in our circumstances as a means of rejuvenating pastures that tend to become worn out, and restoring their mantle of green herbage. In the rotations characteristic of ley farming corn and root crops may occur, but the essential is the laying down, after the last cultivation, of a suitable mixture of grasses and clovers with or without "a nurse crop." The so-called nurse crop behaves only too often as a smother crop and the importance of establishing a good sward for pasture or hay or both is now seen to be so great that, to an increasing extent, farmers are sacrificing the final corn crop and sowing down the grass mixture, often on manured ground that has last produced a root crop.

After all, the grass crop will last for three years or more, depending on the mixture used and the subsequent management, and will yield in a succession of years, after only one cultivation, a volume of food nutrients which far exceeds the measure of any other possible crop—at all events if regard is had to the amount of human labour and expense involved in the various operations of cultivation and harvesting.

The climate and soil of Ireland are ideally suitable for this form of intensive grass cultivation. A New Zealand expert was appointed by the Inter-Party Government as their expert adviser in this matter. He went round the country, and became enthusiastic about the possibilities of the new policy. He saw some very successful and encouraging experiments, but over the greater part of our nearly eight million acres of pasture he saw little but the worst kind of grass flourishing. The extent of the present degeneracy of our pasture land is the measure of the increase in total agricultural output it will be possible to effect when "bent" and scutch grass are as rare as they are now common. After all, "permanent" pasture normally occupies more than two-thirds of our total agricultural land, and must always have been our principal source of agricultural wealth in spite of the fact that our pastures have been traditionally neglected and abused, so that they yielded only a fraction of their potential output.

It is no exaggeration to say that the general adoption of the new grass technique will double the stock-carrying capacity of our land, and bring about a corresponding increase in associated branches of agricultural production, including the output of tillage crops, the total area under which need not be very much reduced.

All this, of course, means curtailing wheat growing for domestic consumption (except in times of international emergency) and concentrating on a livestock policy dependent mainly on grass, fresh or preserved, but supplemented by a programme of tillage, in which forage crops like oats and roots will figure with increasing prominence. The increasing output of livestock and its products will inevitably restore export capacity, to the great advantage of British and other consumers. It is calculated that a modest increase of 25 per cent in agricultural output (which should be realisable within a period of five years) would increase by 100 per cent the surplus available for export, while at the same time making more adequate provision for the domestic consumer.

Already in 1948 there were signs of increase in milk production. The output of cheese threatened to saturate the home market, and an export outlet would have been in request, had it not been necessary to divert increasing milk supplies to butter manufacture, since the latter product was still scarce in the home market.

Of course there are limiting factors. Milch cows, which numbered 1,260,000 in 1939, were only 1,156,000 on 1st June, 1947, but were 1,287,000 on 1st June, 1949. Total cattle were down by nearly 200,000 in 1947 as compared with 1946, and the decrease (81,000) was most marked in the case of cattle under one year. Until the Agreement of 1948 was made it did not pay to rear all the calves that were born. Since that date "dropped" calves of promising quality have sold for upwards of £9 0s. 0d., and none of them are being fed to greyhounds.

The total number of cows and young stock is now steadily increasing, but it will take years to reverse all the effects of the many years which the locusts of war, Economic and International, have eaten.

Meanwhile, the new grass policy is rapidly increasing the output of grass, fresh and preserved, and it seems likely that there will not be enough cattle to eat it all. Hay is the traditional method of preserving grass for winter keep. Hay is reasonably transportable, and does not depreciate overmuch if kept for a year or two. Silage making is rapidly gaining ground. Sweet silage, made from grass or other green crop with molasses, has hitherto been the most usual form of silage made, but the new type of acid silage, known as A.I.V., is now increasing in popularity. This type of silage has long been made in Finland, whence the idea was imported by Dr. Kennedy, of the I.A.O.S., who has pioneered the adoption of this technique in Éire. It is said to preserve almost perfectly the nutriments contained in the fresh grass, and cows fed on it at Mitchelstown Creamery farm in Co. Cork are said to yield nearly four gallons per day without the necessity of feeding "concentrates" to them.

Quite recently a number of persons familiar with the technique of grass drying as practised in England have installed a plant over here. The dried grass, which must be fresh and young, loses four-fifths of its weight in the process, and is finally ground into a very fine meal. It is said to be a complete substitute for concentrates in the feeding of dairy cattle, beef cattle and young stock, and a partial substitute in the case of poultry and pigs. Quantities of this meal are being exported to England. I can foresee the probability that grass production will increase much more rapidly than our cattle numbers, and that this export trade will be one of increasing dimensions. One hopes this is only a temporary phenomenon, as it is much more economic to export the finished product than the raw material. It is. however, a matter for satisfaction that surplus grass, so much a fixture in the form of hay or silage, can be mobilised and transported relatively cheaply in the form of grass meal.

CHAPTER X

(2) Signs of Change in Livestock Policy

FOR about a hundred years Shorthorn cattle have predominated in Irish herds. Originally this was a breed specialised for beef production, but in modern times there has grown up within it a sub-species known as the Dairy Shorthorn. The Creamery Counties, which include six in the south-west and two adjacent to the Border, tend to prefer the Dairy Shorthorn type to any other breed of cattle. The cows of this type are known as "dual purpose" cows. Their surplus male progeny make quite good "stores" and, although not quite as good from the beef point of view as Beef Shorthorns or Herefords, are much in demand by feeders in the dry-stock farming regions which constitute the bulk of central Ireland. Official policy, crystallised in the Live Stock Breeding Act of 1925, has for many generations favoured the preservation and improvement of the dual purpose cow. The reasons for this may be briefly summarised.

The whole agricultural economy of the dry-stock farming counties is dependent on the regular receipt of surplus young cattle born and reared in the Creamery districts. If the latter went over to exclusively dairy breeds like Jerseys or Friesians, which they now show signs of beginning to do, it would mean a revolution in the agricultural practices of the former which might not be effected without serious dislocation and economic loss. There is a well-founded prejudice against Jersey bullocks, and one perhaps equally well-founded against Friesians of that category. On the other hand, Kerry cows are a native dairy breed, and Kerry bullocks are tolerated, and admitted to have their uses as beef producers.

The other important consideration in favour of preserving the dual purpose cow is the fact that normally about 80 per cent of our output of cattle and calves is exported, whereas only about 30 per cent of our dairy produce has at any time been able to find an export outlet. The safety of our balance of payments, and our ability to buy industrial raw materials and finished goods, has traditionally depended to a great extent on our ability to sell store and fat cattle in the British market.   It is argued that if the Creamery Counties go over wholesale to specialised dairy breeds the store cattle trade will be impaired if not ruined.   As against that, it is pointed out that to replace dual purpose cows which only give over 400 gallons a year with Friesians likely to give 1,000 gallons, would mean a vast increase in the production and export of dairy produce.   To which contention the answer is made that we would have to sell these additional quantities of dairy produce in competition with Denmark and New Zealand, whereas we have now a virtual monopoly in the supply of store cattle to the British market.   Official policy has been reluctant to abandon a certainty in favour of a possibility however attractive.

Experts are of opinion that it is possible to grade up the Dairy Shorthorn, by selective breeding and adequate feeding, to a milk output of about 800 gallons without sacrifice of the "conformation" of store progeny.   This is the policy recommended by a majority of the Post-Emergency Committee on Agricultural Policy.   The dairy enthusiasts do not agree, and there are one or two important creameries in the south in which Friesian and even Jersey blood is being introduced to local herds in accordance with locally approved policy.   In a democratic country one cannot, and ought not to try to, prevent such local developments.   There is, however, this to be said.   Ever since the early 1930's the production of butter has been heavily subsidised at the taxpayer's expense.   During the Economic War this was frankly a "producer's subsidy."   The milk supplier got much more than he would have obtained in a free market.   After 1942 the export of butter ceased, and creamery butter was in short supply even on the home market.   The subsidy, now 70/6 per cwt., was a "consumer's subsidy" in the years of scarcity.   In its absence, and in the absence of price control and rationing, the price of butter would have been a famine price, and would have exceeded by a wide margin the total price (including the subsidy) received in those years by creamery suppliers.

However, this was a temporary phenomenon.   A time has

come when the subsidy which still persists is once again a "producer's subsidy," for the home market is now more than saturated with creamery butter. The case for such a subsidy depends essentially on the fact that the dairy industry has hitherto been a key industry, and that the rest of our agricultural economy would fall to pieces without the surplus male progeny of dual purpose cows originating in the Creamery Counties. If the latter go over wholesale to specialised dairy breeds, their industry will become of merely local concern and cease to be a key industry. "Every fish should hang by its own tail" will then be the argument used elsewhere. By all means let the creameries experiment with Friesians, Jersey or other fancy breeds of dairy cattle, but let them do so with their eyes open and a full realisation of all the possible consequences, including the probable loss of the subsidy, which is now increasingly unpopular with the rest of the community.

Apart from these possibilities there is general agreement as to the best and quickest way in which cows may be graded up to a higher level of milk production. Cow testing is officially encouraged and subsidised. The use of "proven sires" is fostered. A "proven sire" is a bull which has been long enough in use to enable the milk-producing capacity of his daughters to be ascertained. Those bulls, whose records in this and other respects are satisfactory, are to be concentrated in artificial insemination centres—now controlled and regulated under the terms of a recent Live Stock (Artificial Insemination) Act, which was one of the last Acts of Mr. De Valera's Government.

Certain creameries in the south have been pioneers in this matter, and had such centres in operation even before the Act was passed. I came across one such centre in 1947 on a farm owned by a creamery near Mallow. Since 1948 the Mitchelstown Creamery has also been maintaining such a centre. In 1948 two of the bulls were Friesian, one a Dairy Shorthorn. In the other there were five Dairy Shorthorn and one Hereford bull. That number was said to be adequate for 1,200 cows.

Selective breeding and adequate feeding are the obvious methods by which milk production may be graded up. The new technique of artificial insemination will play an important part in the former. Already a hopeful beginning has been made.

CHAPTER XI

(3) DEVELOPMENTS IN POULTRY POLICY

THE livestock and other agricultural statistics of Ireland are unique in the fact that they go back with remarkable completeness to 1847. In the matter of livestock they are also unique in the fact that they display a remarkable degree of stability—or inelasticity—throughout the whole period for which they are available. There are, of course, a few exceptions. One of these is poultry. There were less than 6 million poultry in the country now called—or mis-called—Éire in 1851. There was a gradual increase to 14 millions in 1901. In the 1911 census for the first time young poultry were included in the total, and the number jumped to 19 millions, of which total probably nearly 5 millions were young poultry. In subsequent years the highest point reached was 22·9 millions in 1930. Except during the recent World War, when it fell to little over 17 millions, the total tended to fluctuate in the neighbourhood of 20 millions. In 1947 it was 17,300,000. As compared with milch cows, pigs, sheep, horses, and even goats, the total number of poultry has shown a remarkable capacity for expansion. But it has also displayed a regrettable incapacity to pass a maximum figure of about 22 millions. Recent developments in poultry policy, in which Britain has cordially (and financially) co-operated, aim at removing the underlying causes of this incapacity and raising the ceiling of total poultry population very much higher.

Comparisons with other countries indicate the feasibility as well as the desirability of such an aim. In Denmark in 1933 the density of poultry per 1,000 acres of cultivated land was more than twice as great as the density in Éire in 1931 on very small farms, and substantially greater on farms exceeding 100 acres in size. As a result, the value of Danish egg exports in 1938 was more than five times as great as the value of those of Éire. This information is

derived from a paper read by Dr. Beddy to the Statistical
and Social Inquiry Society of Ireland, which is published
in the 1943–44 volume of the Journal.

The experience of Northern Ireland is even more
significant. In 1926 they had less than 8 million poultry
in that country. From 1933 to 1939 the number remained
fairly stable at just over 10 millions. During the recent
World War it rose to 16·6 millions (in 1944), and now
frequently exceeds our total. Evidently "anything we can
do they can do better," a humiliating thought to our
politicians of all parties down here. Of course, this was
partly a phenomenon of availability of feed, of export outlets, and of British price policy, but it was also a phenomenon
of superior technique in poultry production.

One of the last acts of the De Valera régime was to
come to an understanding with the United Kingdom which
brought about an improvement in price. It was not
politically possible to pay quite so high a price as is
currently paid for Northern Ireland eggs, but, to compensate. the United Kingdom agreed to make a substantial
contribution towards the capital cost of putting our whole
poultry and egg production business on a sound scientific
basis. Subsidies are now being paid to approved producers
to lessen the cost to them of acquiring modern poultry
housing and equipment, and to reduce the cost to all poultry
producers of acquiring well-bred young stock. That the
policy is producing results is indicated by the great increase
in the number and capacity of the mammoth incubators
being installed in suitable centres throughout the country.
Co-operative Societies are playing a notable part in this
development. Perhaps one should explain why this
revolution in technique was necessary.

"Total poultry" includes not only "ordinary fowl" but
turkeys, geese and ducks. Recently there has been a great
increase in the number of guinea-fowl produced because they
could be sold at fancy prices to an unrationed market in
Britain. This was an undesirable, but perhaps economically
intelligible, phenomenon of war-time economics. Obviously,
food diverted to such luxury products was not available for
hen-egg production. I do not think guinea-fowl are included
in the official statistics. As regards "ordinary fowl," the
numbers reported on the 1st June, when the census is

taken, consist as to about 40 per cent of young fowl hatched in the previous six months.   Not more than half of these will be pullets, and because of late hatching, by broody hens for the most part, few of these will lay before December. A certain proportion of the other 60 per cent will come to a "sticky" end before December, and most of them will cease to lay by September and not begin before January.   Hence the chronic scarcity of fresh eggs in the autumn and early winter months.   Large-scale early artificial hatching of adequate numbers of pullets is the only way in which this gulf can be bridged.   Early hatched pullets begin to lay in September, just when the older hens knock off.

Reliance on the broody hen, which has hitherto characterised Irish poultry production, just will not produce early hatched pullets, for hens will not go broody before the late spring or early summer.

There are, of course, incubators of 100 egg and 200 egg capacity, but only an exceptional housewife or hen-wife is capable of operating them with success.   It is much easier to buy day-old chicks and rear them with a lamp, or put them under a broody hen, if one is available, that has not a complete quota of her own brood.   Hence, there is an intense demand for these day-old chicks, which are being turned out in rapidly increasing numbers since 1949.

The mammoth incubator is a desirable institution, but it is much better that the increase of total poultry numbers should take place by modest additions to the numbers kept in hundreds of thousands of holdings than by the emergence of a few score highly specialised mammoth poultry farms. The mammoth poultry hatcheries now being installed are quite consistent with this desirable dispersal of total poultry numbers.   The average poultry flock on Irish farms does not exceed 50 birds.   Not more than that number, if indeed as many as that, can be kept with safety to their health, and to the health of other farm stock, in the immediate neighbourhood of the farmyard.   Any serious increase of numbers involves poultry houses, preferably movable, established in pasture land some distance away from the farmyard.   Once this position has been obtained, which involves capital expense, the flock can be increased to 200 or more on all but the smallest holdings with safety and advantage.   The limiting factor till lately was lack of the supplementary rations which are only obtainable from abroad—when obtainable at all.   But, in general, poultry fit in very well with the general scheme of Irish farming.   Domestic supplies of potatoes, skim-milk, wheaten bye-products, and oats go a long way in feeding them.

The new poultry policy aims at getting over this first hurdle.   Once the habit of housing appropriate numbers of poultry in open fields has become general, subsequent expansion will take care of itself.   Poultry houses so situated are as common a sight in Northern Ireland as they are still a rare one in the south.

Very large flocks of poultry are a possible development in some cases, but they bring their own peculiar dangers and problems.   Poultry producers in such cases are entirely at the mercy of the ratio between the cost of feed and the price of poultry products.   So large a proportion of their raw materials must be bought.   More important still, it is precisely in such large flocks that the most serious and infectious poultry diseases, many of them formerly unheard of, are apt to break out.   Some of these diseases, e.g. bacillary white diarrhœa, familiarly known as B.W.D., are transmissible through the eggs of "carrier" hens, which themselves have somehow managed to survive the onset of the microbe.

Special steps are enforced under our new Poultry Hatcheries Act to ensure that only eggs from "approved egg supply farms," where the hens have been blood tested, will be used in our new large-scale poultry hatcheries. Otherwise the sale of day-old chicks from such sources to numerous poultry producers might introduce new diseases and cause widespread devastation among existing poultry flocks.

In general, it seemed reasonable to look for substantial results from the new poultry policy, which is the policy of the present as well as of the former Éire Government, and in which the British Government has taken a practical and helpful interest.   But in 1951 the prospect became much more obscure.   The price of Indian meal rose to more than 30 shillings a cwt.   The Ministry of Food offers only two shillings a dozen for Éire eggs.   The price ratio has gone "haywire," and we are in 1951 abandoning the policy of expansion, no doubt with considerable loss to many recently created vested interests.

I

CHAPTER XII

The Progress of Mechanisation

U P till 1939 Irish agriculture was comparatively little mechanised and up till 1932 hardly at all. The principal test for the degree of mechanisation is the number of agricultural tractors in use. Nearly all the more elaborate modern implements for field use require tractor power for their operation. Most of them cannot conveniently be pulled by horses and many of them are designed exclusively for tractors.

The statistical data relating to agricultural tractors in Éire before 1939 are somewhat uncertain. According to the Irish Trade Journal of June, 1948, there were in 1939 2,067 tractors available. In England and Wales, with not much more than twice the agricultural acreage, there were in 1939 48,750 tractors. In April, 1948, there were 9,781 tractors in Éire, and the number, rapidly growing, was in 1950 12,000. By 1944 England and Wales had 135,000 tractors—nearly three times the pre-war number—so, relatively speaking, the degree of mechanisation is very much higher in England than in Éire. Nevertheless, the mechanisation of Irish agriculture is now well under way. It is interesting to speculate on the social and economic readjustments which it is likely to occasion.

An important fact about the Irish agricultural economy is that 74·2 per cent of the holdings of 5 acres or more are under 50 acres in area. They cover 35·3 per cent of the available agricultural land. It follows that the owners of three-quarters of the holdings are not likely to be interested in the ownership of tractors for exclusive use on their own farms. There are, however, some 70,000 or 80,000 farmers whose holdings exceed 50 acres in size, and they own about two-thirds of the total agricultural area.

It is also a well-known fact that a higher proportion of total farm land is usually ploughed in farms of 50 acres or less than in those exceeding 50 acres in size. In fact, the idea prevails in certain quarters that practically all the tillage farming is done on the smaller farms, and that the owners of the larger farms do no tillage at all (apart from compulsory tillage in war time), and are mere graziers or "ranchers." This is not in accordance with the evidence contained in "Agricultural Statistics, 1847–1926," p. xliv. The decline in the proportion of land ploughed is quite gentle up to the 200 acre size, and even the owners of farms of greater size than that do substantial amounts of tillage. More interesting from our present point of view is the fact that between 1874 and 1912 there was a decline of 31 per cent in the area ploughed on farms in the 15 to 30 acres size group, whereas the decline was only 7 per cent on farms between 100 and 200 acres in size. More surprising still— there was an increase of 27 per cent in the area ploughed on farms *over* 500 acres in size between those two dates. Evidently tillage is becoming relatively more important on the large holding and relatively less important on the small holding. This is a tendency which the modern mechanisation of farming is likely to accelerate, with perhaps revolutionary consequences.

Elsewhere it is a generally accepted fact that the low-cost production of tillage crops is only possible on large holdings suitably laid out and well equipped with the most modern power-operated machinery. During the Economic War our farmers on the larger farm sizes had a bad time. Everything possible was done for the small farmer, who is mainly a processor of raw materials into pigs and poultry, and normally produces only a small proportion of these raw materials on his own farm. In those days the small farmer could make a living, for there was no limit to available raw materials, and the prices of his finished products were suitably adjusted to the cost of the former. Under World War conditions the boot was on the other foot. The "large" farmer who had managed to remain solvent after the Economic War, and was adequately equipped, could turn out cash crops at a minimum cost and profit by the steadily rising prices which had to be adjusted to the circumstances of the "small" ill-equipped farmer. The latter had perforce to curtail his activities in raising pigs and poultry (from which normally he derived an important part of his income) and rely on the sale of farm crops for an increasing proportion of his receipts.

Agricultural labour has shared in the general prosperity of the larger farmers, and agricultural wages have doubled since 1939. Mechanised farming undoubtedly increases output per man, and therefore the continuation of high wages into the post-war era, especially if there is a fall in agricultural prices, depends on the process of mechanisation being carried to its economically optimum conclusion. A situation may then exist in which the agricultural labourer in good employment is better off in every way than the "small" farmer with a large family, if indeed it does not already exist.

The latter will perhaps profit by the new knowledge about intensive grass cultivation. Here, again, the practice of the appropriate technique requires access to, if not the ownership of, power machinery. The re-seeding of worn out pastures is a simple matter when you can command the services of a tractor and a disc harrow. The making of grass silage is quick and easy if you have a power-operated grass "pick-up" and a grass elevator to feed the grass into the silo, or, better still, a power-operated "buck rake." There are not many disc harrows in Éire and relatively few tractors. Unless one farms "in a large way" it is not economic to own such things for one's own exclusive use.

In practice, one can sometimes borrow and one can often hire. But a more theoretically perfect solution of the problem is the co-operative ownership of such implements and power units by groups of farmers. A co-operative implement society which is *only* an implement society has many difficulties to contend with. Where will the machines be housed and cared for when not in use? Who will be responsible for their servicing? Since everyone is likely to want the same machine at the same time, how will the order of priority in such use be determined?

A number of creameries in the South of Ireland have bought farms which they run on a commercial basis. They equip them in the most modern way, and the machinery they own is available for hiring out to members as well as for use on the common farm. The members have other interests in common besides the common ownership of implements, and the jealousies about priority of use which are apt to break up *mere* implement societies are said to cause no inconvenience in such more highly organised societies.

In parishes and neighbourhoods where there are no financially strong co-operative societies it would seem necessary, if the most modern implements are to be put in the hands of all our farmers, that they should combine to acquire the ownership in common of a parochial or co-operative farm, equip it more than adequately, appoint a farm manager and staff for its commercial exploitation, and have their parish machinery pool in association with their parochial farm for housing and servicing.

Irish farms are notoriously ill-equipped by all modern standards. According to Dr. Beddy, in the Journal of the Statistical and Social Inquiry Society of Ireland, 1943–44, Denmark, pre-1939, with two-thirds of our agricultural area, had nearly ten times the number of corn drills and five times the number of harvesters that we had. According to my own calculations, published in the 1941–42 volume of the same journal, instrumental capital per acre averaged only £2 0s. 0d. in value at 1939 prices.

The other day I came across an Irish farmer of 75 acres. In his first two years he had already spent £1,025 on a tractor and implements, but had not yet bought a harvester. Dovea Creamery Farm, with 380 acres of farm, has acquired about £2,300 worth of agricultural machinery and implements. It looks as if the larger farm would require instrumental capital worth from £5 to £10 per acre at post-war prices. But a 20 acre farm with only £100 or £200 worth of such capital would be quite inadequately equipped. It is not financially possible, or economically desirable, that every one of our 300,000 farmers should personally own all the equipment he would need to use. But it would be quite feasible to equip a few thousand co-operatively owned farms with machinery and implements amply sufficient for the cultivation of the common farm, and for all the requirements of its associated owners on the farms which they own in an individual capacity.

CHAPTER XIII

WOMEN ON THE FARM

IN the 1936 Census Report the total number of persons returned as being farmers, by way of principal occupation, is 259,000. Of these, 213,000 are male and 46,000 female. The number of farmers' sons and daughters "assisting on home farm" was at that date 191,000, of whom 146,000 were sons and 45,000 were daughters. The number of "Other Relatives" returned as similarly occupied was 53,000—the number of males being 39,000 and females 14,000. Thus altogether 105,000 women are officially regarded as concerned in farm work in a total of 503,000 "Farmers and Relatives assisting on home farm." The number of wage-paid employees amounted to 141,000, of whom only 1,100 were women.

Thus about 20 per cent of family workers in agriculture are women. It is not certain whether the statistical net is cast wide enough to include all such workers. It may be that many women who "give a hand" on the farm as well as in the house are returned as statistically "unoccupied."

However, there is no gainsaying the statistical and practical importance of women's work in the scheme of Irish agriculture. The more important question is as to whether their importance, actual and potential, is sufficiently recognised, and whether their specific contribution is all that it might be. This is not merely an economic question, but one of social organisation and human relationships. In dealing with it not much direct assistance will be obtained from cold-blooded statistical data. The latter, however, do indicate that the persistent "flight from the land" is to a greater extent a flight of female rather than male personnel. In rural districts the number of males exceeds the number of females by a wide margin. The marriage rate in rural Ireland is the lowest in Europe.

Any broad generalisations are subject to many exceptions and must be based very largely on personal impressions. The Anglo-Irish gentry of the eighteenth century established a social tradition which still persists, and has tended to penetrate downwards in the social pyramid. It implies a gay and careless attitude to life, in which fox-hunting,' dancing and dining—nowadays tennis, badminton and cocktail drinking as well—played a notable part. Those individuals, and they were many, who spent their capital as well as their income on such light-hearted activities, were an object of sympathy rather than of social reprobation to the neighbours. The attitude to life displayed by women, especially young women, plays a notable part in determining the social values current in any society. No one grudges the young people a good time, but it is important economically as well as socially that the more expensive forms of amusement should not be indulged in to excess. It is also most desirable that the education of women, in all ranks of rural society, should be so directed that they will find the many activities open to them, on the farm and in the home, intrinsically interesting as well as economically productive. There are important and influential movements in operation which have this end in view. The Irish Country-women's Association is one such and the organisation known as "Muintir na Tire" is another.

There are some fourteen "Rural Domestic Economy Schools" exclusively for women students. They are under the control of various religious orders of women and are subsidised by the State. The number of students attending such schools in 1947–48 would appear to be about 400. They are, of course, residential establishments. No doubt they do useful work in preparing girls to play a part in farm life, if they return to it, or to become poultry or domestic economy instructresses, for which occupations there is an expanding demand. But in the nature of the case they cannot be co-educational, and they cannot reproduce any approximation to the atmosphere of real farm life. They must be essentially specialised institutions. It is important that women should have a scientific appreciation, not only of the specialised contributions they can make to the success of agriculture, but also of the part played by the latter in the general economy of the farm. This they can only acquire at a co-educational Agricultural School.

One such establishment has been founded under Methodist auspices in 1947. It is known as Gurteen Agricultural College, and is situated at Ballingarry, in Co. Tipperary. Although it is a Protestant Institution, its educational work has, as a matter of course, been encouraged and subsidised by the Government in a manner and spirit that has been much appreciated by its founders. It is, indeed, unique in many ways. Not only is it the only establishment in Éire in which girls belonging to the religious minority can acquire the kind of rural education which is available for members of the majority religion in the Rural Domestic Economy Schools mentioned above. State-managed Agricultural Colleges are, of course, open to members of all religions, but none of them quite fulfils the need for which Gurteen now caters. It is also unique in being co-educational as well as residential. The former "Big House," now taken over and adapted, lent itself admirably to the accommodation of both sexes, with due regard to the proprieties, while at the same time providing the domestic conditions for organised farm life and work, and organised studies appropriate to the needs of both sexes. There were 13 girls and 27 boys in residence during the 1947–48 session. Three of the staff are women, one of them a teacher of dairying and poultry management; another taught domestic economy, while a third provided instruction in cooking, laundry, needlework and housewifery. Incidentally, she presided over one of the cleanest, best equipped and most attractive kitchens I have ever seen.

As for poultry, there were at the time of my visit only 300 hens as well as some ducks and turkeys. They are housed in modern hen-houses some distance away from the farmyard. The number of poultry was to be expanded as soon as the necessary additional houses could be erected. The aim is to have 1,000 birds or more, and to run them as pedigree birds, surplus young stock being disposed of throughout the country for breeding purposes. Electric light, made on the farm, is available, but only small oil-burning incubators are used. No mammoth hatchery business is contemplated, and, therefore, no trade in day-old chicks. The farm was in process of acquiring an

AERIAL VIEW OF GURTEEN AGRICULTURAL COLLEGE

adequate complement of poultry, since, for teaching purposes, poultry at all stages of maturity are required.

During my visit the Principal, Rev. J. W. McKinney, was unfortunately absent on holiday. As only two permanent farm labourers are kept on the farm, which contains 308 acres, most of the work at all times is done by the students. The education is thoroughly practical. Although it was holiday time, in August, 1948, eight of the boys and four of the girls remained in residence to do the ordinary routine "chores" under the supervision of the farm manager.

One could not help being impressed by the friendly spirit of "cameraderie" that existed between all concerned. It was just one large happy family. If any of these boys and girls elect to strike up a life partnership, and practice a joint agricultural profession elsewhere so much the better. The qualities of the woman concerned mean more than 50 per cent of the success of any farming enterprise anywhere. Any girl who has imbibed the atmosphere of Gurteen Agricultural College, and learnt not only her own job but to appreciate the larger problems of agricultural practice in which men are more specifically concerned, will make an ideal farmer's wife. It is a pity that there is only one Gurteen, but its success, which is already assured, will doubtless lead to the establishment of many others. No better use could be made of the Big Houses, many of them now derelict, which were an architectural feature of a system of land tenure now happily passed away.

A word or two about the farm itself might also be of interest. Before being acquired by the College it had been cruelly exploited for many years. Seven straw crops in successive years had been taken off one particular field. That field was finally a mass of weeds. The farm manager told me he had to plough it seven times the previous winter with his most powerful tractor in order to bury and kill the weeds. After suitable treatment with artificial manures and lime it had in 1948 been re-seeded with an appropriate grass mixture. The result was said to be quite promising.

The past history of this farm, typical of many such in Éire, reminds me of the story of the large farm, bought largely by means of a bank loan unwisely made to an improvident farmer. When things were obviously going from bad to worse on the farm the latter was asked by a friend how he could sleep at night on account of the worry of the large loan. He replied that he never lost any sleep at all on that account, but he often wondered how the bank manager could sleep at all!

The story epitomises a point of view which has been a major curse of Irish agriculture. I would like to feel that it illustrates a state of mind now happily non-existent, but some of the worst features of the eighteenth-century tradition have remarkable powers of survival.

CHAPTER XIV

THREE CO-OPERATIVELY OWNED FARMS

(1) DRINAGH (1948)

THE village of Drinagh is situated about five miles south of Dunmanway "as the crow flies." Unfortunately, as Tom Casement might have said, I was driving a 12 H.P. Morris car and not a crow. The roads may possibly suit the latter form of transport.

The central creamery in Drinagh must be one of the largest in Ireland. It was established in 1923 and has fifteen auxiliaries. The most westerly is at Bantry, a good twenty miles away. The operations of the Society extend equally far in an easterly direction. Owing to the high ground on the south towards Clonakilty, and the range of mountains north of the valley of the Bandon River, the north-south axis of its activities would be only a matter of ten miles on the average. There are 1,600 suppliers, for the most part members, and the total milk supply provided in 1947 approximated to three and a half million gallons. The average milk supply from each supplier was somewhat in excess of 2,000 gallons. Apparently about four or five cows per farm are the usual complement on local farms if they keep the ordinary Dairy Shorthorn. However, there is a certain disposition in the neighbourhood to go over to Jersey cattle. The Society keeps a Jersey bull on their farm but no Shorthorn bull. Only butter is made in the creamery. The members want all the skim milk they can get and take it all home. Official statistics indicate that the whole of County Cork is a region in which pigs and poultry are relatively dense. In 1926 there were twelve pigs per 100 acres of crops and pasture in County Cork, only four in County Clare, and two in County Meath. As for poultry, there were in 1926 twenty-one per 10 acres of crops and pasture in County Cork, ten in County Clare, and ten in Meath. Density of pigs and poultry is closely cor-

related with density of milch cows. There were fifteen cows
per 100 acres of crops and pasture in County Cork in 1926, ten
in County Clare, and three in County Meath. With regard
to dry cattle over two years, there is a reverse correlation—
five in County Cork in that year, and, at the other extreme,
twenty-four in County Meath per 100 acres of crops and
pasture.

To judge from their published balance sheet, the
Drinagh Society enjoys a strong financial position. Assets
amount to £144,000, and exceed paid-up share capital and
liabilities by £55,000. Their trading account aggregated
£442,000 in 1947, but it is difficult to determine to what
extent this was represented by milk processing activities and
by the many other activities of the Society. For, in
addition to the manufacture of butter, the Society maintains
a general supply store in which not only farm production
requirements are sold, but also groceries and draperies. It
also runs a scutch mill for flax, which gives seasonal employment to as many as sixty hands. For some reason or other
the growing of flax, which is almost unknown in Éire except
in the Border counties, persists in this region of County
Cork as well as in North Mayo—both far away from centres
of linen manufacture. The price for scutched flax in 1947,
arranged between the Éire and the British Government,
varied from 33 shillings to 42 shillings per stone, according
to grade. The Northern Ireland growers received in 1947
a higher price for similar qualities. This is another example
of price discrimination. There is no justification for paying
a lower price to the Éire grower, for flax is an exhausting
crop, not only to the soil, but to the human labour concerned
with growing and "retting" it, whether the labour is
"family" or hired.

The Society pays in wages some £20,000 per annum and
employs 103 workers. Its activities include the grinding of
maize and home-grown grain for the account of its members.
Since 1946 it has operated a poultry hatchery. As was
happening elsewhere in numerous instances, plant capacity
in this department was being rapidly expanded in 1948.
Their 12,000 egg incubator was being replaced by an 18,000
egg one. The availability of Shannon current facilitated
these activities and developments. Some day, perhaps, the
debt we owe to the pioneers who established a national

electricity service, at a time when it implied a great deal of faith, will be fully realised and adequately expressed. When the present Rural Electrification Scheme is complete, many additional attractive social and economic possibilities will doubtless become actualities.

In 1943 the Society acquired a fifty-acre farm adjacent to the creamery premises. It had a problem of sewage disposal. The washing out of creamery premises is apt to leave a smell outside. It is much better to fertilise land directly or indirectly from this source than to offend human nostrils or poison fish. There were difficulties and delays in the process of modernising the farm owing to the prevailing scarcity of supplies. However, a foreman and two farm workers were in 1948 comfortably installed in a reconstructed dwelling-house lighted by electricity. Fifty-five pigs and five breeding sows were housed in "Ctesiphon" structures, as recommended by Mr. McGuckian, the great pig expert from Northern Ireland. Successful experiments on the re-seeding of worn out pastures had been carried out. Grass silos had been erected and were in use. In 1947 "sweet" silage was made with molasses, but the protein content was poor. In 1948 they tried the new acid or A.I.V. system of silage making. This is now becoming quite a cult, thanks largely to the propaganda initiated by Dr. Kennedy of the I.A.O.S. It is not unfair to say that the Department of Agriculture experts were rather inclined to go slow with A.I.V. experiments. No amount of propaganda could have achieved the present results if Dr. Kennedy had not succeeded in persuading some enterprising creameries to try the new method on their farms. Several of them did so and all are enthusiastic about their experience. There is much to be said for a number of experimental farms, run co-operatively on a commercial basis, in which the spirit of enterprise will test out new ideas by the criterion of profit, and the dead hand of officialdom will be conspicuously absent.

There are fourteen cows and a bull on the Drinagh Creamery farm as well as some young stock. This is quite a large stock for a fifty-acre farm to carry—not to mention the pigs. However, the pigs must be fed largely on bought in materials, and therefore their presence really increases the capacity of the farm to carry other stock.

A threshing "mill," a binder, a tractor, a manure distributor, a tractor mower and a cultivator were maintained by the Society, mainly for hiring out to members. A new milking machine imported from New Zealand, known as the G.V.B., was in use on the creamery farm. It is used in a special milking shed, into which the cows are driven for milking, and thus is not, like other milking machinery, a permanent fixture in the cow-house. This is claimed to be a more sanitary arrangement.

Another machine shown to me by Mr. Morgan, to whom I owe most of this information, was also at the time unique in Ireland. It is a marvellous rotating platform, the hopper of which greedily absorbs hundredweights of butter, while a man stands by and takes delivery of half-pound packages of butter neatly wrapped in butter-paper and labelled with the Society's trade mark.

Unfortunately I was unable to visit Drinagh in a subsequent year.

(2) KANTURK (1948).

The town of Kanturk is a little bit off the track of a person proceeding by road or rail from Mallow to Killarney. If, however, a motorist decided to turn south and proceed *via* Millstreet to Macroom he could hardly help passing through Kanturk. About a mile to the south of the latter he would observe a tall square castle, obviously a ruin, but with quite a lot of it still standing. If he consulted Lewis' Topographical Dictionary he would find that it had been built by MacDonagh Carthy in Elizabeth's reign but was never completed, because the Government of the day thought it had too many of the characteristics of a fortress.

In 1837 corn, pigs, sheep and cattle were important local products. They still are. The town had then 1,349 inhabitants. It had 1,377 in 1926 and 1,339 in 1936. But the District Electoral Division in which the town is situated had 2,045 inhabitants in 1926 and 2,082 in 1936. Evidently rural population is increasing in this neighbourhood—a rare phenomenon.

Kanturk lies some miles north of the upper waters of the Blackwater—the river is well named. A branch of the Mallow-Killarney Railway runs north from Banteer Junction

to Newmarket and passes Kanturk on the way. But it is
now derelict. It was on the list for extinction along with
the Fermoy-Mitchelstown Branch and a host of others in
1938, and since then the directors of our railway system have
had their way with these two branches anyhow. I gather
that the Kanturk people miss their railway service. However, C.I.E. lorries do much of the transport for the town
and the local creamery, and perhaps the directors have no
reason to regret their decision.

I wonder were they equally wise in closing down the
Fermoy-Mitchelstown Branch. As we shall see, the volume
of production and commerce associated with Mitchelstown
Creamery is considerable, and tends constantly to increase.
Practically all the creamery's transport is done by road in
lorries owned by the Society. They deliver their produce
by road as far away as Dublin and Sligo. A similar situation
exists with regard to the important creamery at Mallow,
which is not on a branch but on a main line. One would like
to know why C.I.E. appears to be able to give satisfactory
road service at Kanturk and elsewhere in South Cork whereas
other important creameries prefer to provide their own road
transport.

Kanturk Creamery was founded in 1926. It has five
auxiliaries and 480 suppliers, of whom 350 are members. It
has a milk supply of nearly 2 million gallons. Its principal
activity is the manufacture of butter, the skim milk being
returned to the suppliers for use on their farms. During
the Economic War the suppliers did not want all the available
skim milk. The export outlet for pigs, poultry products,
and cattle was seriously obstructed, and production of livestock products on the farm correspondingly discouraged.
This led to an interesting development. The Society decided
to turn surplus skim milk into casein plastic, which is an
admirable raw material for the manufacture of buttons and
beads. The process of producing casein begins just as in
cheese manufacture. But when the curd has had all the
moisture extracted under heat and pressure it becomes a fine
dry powder which not even the rats would eat. After
further processing and dyeing in the desired colours it comes
out as flat slabs, for button manufacture, or hard tubular
shapes suitable for the manufacture of beads. During the
second World War the availability of this locally manu-

factured raw material enabled twelve hundred persons to continue in industrial employment elsewhere who might otherwise have been idle.   The Society was in 1949 in a position to develop an export trade—to France and elsewhere—in this product, but there were currency difficulties in the way.

The Creamery Manager, Mr. O'Keeffe, to whom I owe much of this information, assured me that the milk supply in 1948 showed an increase of 12 per cent on its 1947 level. He attributed this to the better weather and to the more extensive use of fertilisers on the grass land—then at long last possible.   This confirms an impression I had already formed.   The increase of our milk supply, and therefore of all our most important agricultural production is primarily a question of lime and phosphates.   To parody the famous Danton—what we need, if we are rapidly to restore our capacity to export butter, is "encore des phosphates et toujours des phosphates."

In 1944 the Society acquired a 50-acre farm with a view to solving the problem of surplus whey.   The farm had some buildings but no dwelling-house, and the land was utterly derelict.   The restoration of a derelict farm to a high state of fertility has great educational value for all concerned.   The neighbours learn by personal observation what can be done by modern technique and the application of up to date scientific knowledge to make the "desert blossom like the rose."   A visit to Glasnevin or Athenry is apt to leave the impression that anyone could show good results if he had land like that to farm and the taxpayer at his back.

A lot of new building was going on at the farm when I visited it.   Modern accommodation had been provided for 320 pigs, including 30 young sows.   The Society planned to breed pigs as well as fatten bought in "bonhams." Ultimately, a pig population of 600 is contemplated.   A liquid manure tank had been delivered but was not yet in position.   Meanwhile, the sewage from the pig pens was flowing down and fertilising one of the finest fields of thistles I have ever seen.

In the course of 1946–47 three fields of old worn-out pasture were ploughed up and re-seeded direct from pasture.   But before sowing down they were treated with an ample supply of pig manure and lime.   The results were thoroughly satisfactory. During the first season (which means within two or three months of sowing) the re-seeded fields were grazed with lambs. This, of course, is standard practice in re-seeding technique. You must not cut hay the first year and you must not graze with heavy stock. Otherwise the sward will become "puddled." Calves or sheep will tramp the surface into a firm consistency and not leave any hoof marks.

In 1948 twelve heifers and a Friesian bull replaced the sheep on the established new pasture. Electric current is available, and a milking machine was about to be installed. There have been difficulties about supplies and building materials, and this farm, like the one at Milford, must be seen with the eye of faith.

The Society has long been in the habit of keeping expensive agricultural machines for hiring out to its members. It has a threshing "mill," two tractors, two disc-harrows, two binders and two two-furrow ploughs. Consequently, its own farm will start with an adequate supply of power and mechanical equipment. The disc-harrow is of great importance in any re-seeding programme, especially if old pasture is being ploughed up for re-seeding. Without it it is impossible to get a suitable seed bed. The ordinary spike-tooth harrow is apt to bring old grass and weeds to the surface. But the disc-harrow requires a lot of power. It is pre-eminently a tractor-operated harrow. Consequently, the development of our new policy of ley farming and intensive grass cultivation must be closely associated with an increase in the number of tractors and disc-harrows.

(3) MILFORD (1948).

Milford is most conveniently reached *via* Charleville. The creamery here was founded in 1887, so it is one of the oldest in Ireland. It is a central creamery with two auxiliaries, or cream-separating stations, and draws its supplies from a maximum radius of about eight miles. In 1947 it received about one and a half million gallons of milk, most of which was turned into butter and some into cheese. In winter, when liquid milk supplies in Dublin are short,

Milford is one of the creameries from which milk, presumably pasteurised, is sent all the way to Dublin.

To judge from its balance sheet, its financial position is thoroughly sound and very liquid. Property and assets worth nearly £40,000 on 31st December, 1947, exceed paid-up capital and liabilities by £26,000. The value of stock-in-trade was three times as high as the small bank overdraft of £4,066 10s. 3d. There is evidently no financial obstacle to the spirit of enterprise which the Society is apt to display.

For some years it has been doing a miscellaneous trade in agricultural goods on behalf of its members. It grinds meal and mills flour for them. It sells feeding stuffs (when available), and no doubt would sell more if it could get them. It maintains a saw-mill, at which members can get trunks of trees (supplied by themselves) cut up into suitable lengths of timber. It collects and buys eggs from members and suppliers for distribution through the wholesale trade to ultimate consumers.

This side of its business is likely to develop considerably in the near future and perhaps experience some modification. Shannon electric current is available, which means that poultry hatching by electricity is a possibility. In fact, it became an actuality in February, 1948, when a 2,000 egg incubator was set in operation. At the time of my visit (August, 1948) a new one to hold 18,000 eggs had been delivered and was about to be installed. This is one of many centres in which the new poultry-hatching policy—initiated by the Government of Mr. De Valera—appears to be making rapid strides. In this, as in other important respects, the new "Inter-Party" Government has caused no innovation in economic policy.

An 18,000 egg incubator will presumably produce between 50,000 and 60,000 chicks in a season, and will require more than that number of hatching eggs. Judging from the published accounts, the Society bought about 150,000 eggs in 1947 for all purposes. It looks as if a high proportion of the locally available eggs will in future command the higher price paid for hatching eggs—if the producers can qualify as "approved egg supply farms" under the Poultry Hatcheries Act, 1947.

The Society has also been functioning as an Agricultural

Implement Society. It owns four tractors, one disc-harrow, three two-furrow ploughs, three binders and three threshing "mills." Hitherto these had been used exclusively for hiring out to members, but quite lately the Society acquired a farm of its own. As elsewhere, it was partly a question of the economic disposal of whey. The farmers take home some, but not all the whey that resulted from cheese-making. The farm is situated a mile away along the Charleville road, past Kilbolane Castle,[4] a ruin which owes much of its present picturesque appearance to the doings of Oliver Cromwell— a noted Republican of the seventeenth century. The farm contains 150 statute acres and has undoubted possibilities, but time will be required before they can be realised. The usual crops were being cultivated, and twenty cows, with the usual complement of young stock, were being maintained. The emphasis is on pigs, of which there are 200 housed in the porcine, equivalent of a modern luxury hotel—just as at Mitchelstown. No sows or boars are kept. The pigs are bought in as "bonhams" from the members and fattened by the Society. This is a natural division of labour which suggests itself, though elsewhere breeding as well as fattening is practised on these large-scale pig farms.

The whey is conveyed in huge metal tanks, rather like a petrol distributing lorry, and is fed into concrete tanks adjacent to each pig-pen. The pigs drink gallons of it and would wallow in it if allowed.

Dwelling accommodation for farm personnel is limited and inadequate. There is a small dairy-house which is being reconstructed. A new silo was also in evidence, but a great deal of reconstruction still remained to be done. The farm buildings had to be looked on with the eye of faith. Three farm workers were permanently employed on the farm, and, as there are forty creamery workers who are not too busy in the winter, some of these are diverted to farm work, and are doubtless very useful in works of maintenance, improvement, and reconstruction.

The farm had not been long enough in operation in 1948 to have any interesting experiments in re-seeding to show. However, the presence of a new silo indicated that the

---

[4] Readers of *Bowenscourt* will remember the part played by Kilbolane Castle in the history of Dr. Elizabeth Bowen's family.

management is grass-minded.   I anticipate that it will follow much the same cycle of development as Mitchelstown with a gradually increasing emphasis on cows and grass, but with pigs continuing to play an essential part.

Mr. Noonan, the manager, was absent on holiday when I called, but his assistant, Mr. Stritch, gave me all possible facilities and information.

CHAPTER XV

A "Workhouse" that is a Workhouse

NOT far from Rathdowney there is a disused work-house. Every traveller in Ireland must have noticed buildings such as this. They all belong to the same period of architecture—early nineteenth-century—and are very solidly built. They suggest perhaps the characteristics of a jail rather than of a modern luxury hotel. In these days of "cheap" building, that is only cheap to look at, one cannot withhold a certain tribute of admiration for these old workhouses whatever their present use.

It is not immediately obvious why Donaghmore Work-house (Leix County) was established just there, near the very small village of Donaghmore, and more or less half-way between the important town of Rathdowney and the railway junction of Ballybrophy. Ballybrophy's only title to fame is that here the railway traveller on his way to Cork may change his mind and go on to Limerick instead.

Anyhow, Donaghmore Workhouse is no longer a work-house within the meaning of the Poor Law Acts, but has been leased to the Donaghmore Co-operative Creamery, Ltd., and is now a hive of industry, and therefore a workhouse in every important sense. It was established as a creamery about twenty years ago. Being more or less on the edge of the region in which dairy farming is a speciality, it never received a really adequate supply of milk. The maximum appears to have been 464,000 gallons in 1935—in 1947 only 144,000 gallons. Other creameries, like the Centenary Creamery, Thurles, get over 1 million gallons in the year. There are 500 members, and the amount of capital they have paid up is £4,650. In the earlier years of its existence its margin of net profit was pretty slender—about £100— and in one year (1935) it showed a small loss. After 1937 the volume of milk received began a serious downward trend, which was checked and reversed quite recently. But the Society would have been in a bad way if it had not branched out in 1938 into a number of diverse activities, the profits from which more than counter-balance the continuing losses on butter manufacture.   It is interesting to note that in 1935 the Society was paying 4·12 pence per gallon for milk, skim milk being returned to suppliers, and got 464,000 gallons.   In 1947 it paid 14·42 pence, and got only 144,000 gallons.   In 1935 it got 11·86 pence per lb. for butter sold, and in 1947 about three times as much, 33·25 pence. Evidently the substantial increase in the price paid for milk did not prevent a serious reduction in the milk supply, and the causes of the latter must be sought in other directions.

In 1938 the Society took up the trade in agricultural goods, the turnover in which totalled £27,000 in that year, as against £7,600 for dairy produce.   In 1947 the turnover in agricultural goods was nearly £100,000 and dairy produce £15,000.   Much of this considerable expansion of turnover was carried on at a very fine margin of profit.   Nevertheless, net profit per annum, which had been of the order of £100 before 1938, has since 1945 approached and passed the £1,500 level.   Undoubtedly the Society has strengthened its financial position, as well as greatly increased its usefulness to its members, by expanding and diversifying its business activities.   Let us see what some of these ancillary activities now are.

The Society owns a tractor, a disc-harrow and a harvester, the use of which is hired out to members as required. Actually it can get around about forty of them in this way —a small proportion perhaps, but many of the rest either do not require this service or can obtain it more conveniently from private contractors.   The Society owns no land of its own, and can therefore have no economic use for expensive agricultural machinery except for hiring out to members. As we shall see elsewhere, societies which own and operate a farm of their own can maintain a greater volume and variety of modern agricultural equipment, can demonstrate its use as well as other aspects of modern scientific farming on their own farms, and thus dovetail the requirements of the co-operative farm into those of their members' own farms, and create an appetite for better farming all round.

Mr. Dillon will get no further with his offer to finance Parish Council owned agricultural implements unless he is willing to finance the acquisition of parochially owned experimental farms to serve a purpose similar to that of creamery owned farms.

The Donaghmore Society buys grain from its members, maintains a seed cleaning and processing department, and sells seeds and manures of guaranteed quality to its members. It also grinds wheat and (when it can get it) Indian corn for its members. Before 1939 it disposed of about 30 tons a week of maize in this way. In 1949 its allotment was 18 cwt. a month. This is typical of the scarcity of imported feed at that date.

A few years ago the Society established a hardware store in its premises, in which are now sold cement, buckets, spades, chains, harrows, harness and all the miscellaneous articles that farmers need in connection with their work. They did this for the greater convenience of their members. It saves time and transport to take home what you want when you must go to the creamery every day, anyhow, with your milk. The practice followed was to add about 25 per cent to the wholesale price, and then it appeared they were selling about 30 per cent cheaper than similar goods were being sold by local merchants. I don't know if any agitation was raised up in consequence of this, but I do know that in every centre where farmers have improved their own economic position by taking co-operative control of commerce and processing the local merchants have in the long run benefited indirectly but substantially.

The Donaghmore Society is fortunate in having the Shannon electric current available. This has made possible the establishment of a poultry hatchery department. In 1947 it had an 8,000 egg incubator in operation and it sold 25,000 live chicks. That was a difficult time for artificial hatching by electricity, for during the Arctic spell in the early part of that year the Shannon current was cut off for five days. However, Mr. Grogan and his fellow-workers rose to the occasion. They worked night and day, filling barrels with hot water to place beneath the incubators and keeping them replenished, and managed to save the bulk of the 8,000 eggs that were at stake.

Poultry hatching by electricity seems likely to be a rapidly expanding business. The Donaghmore Society installed a new 16,000 egg incubator in 1947—thus doubling their prospective output to meet an expanding demand, and similar developments were taking place elsewhere. No public electricity supply is completely immune from the danger of "load shedding." It would be just too bad if £1,000 worth of eggs and chicks were ruined in consequence. The Donaghmore Society have, of course, an automatic thermostatically controlled alarm bell and the manager lives on the premises. But they also plan to instal this year a petrol-driven "stand-by" electricity generating plant which can be switched on if and when the Shannon current should fail.

I had meant to say something more about the premises. They are so large and commodious that most of them are still unoccupied. When the Society wants to start a new activity all it has to do is to modernise and "civilise" another portion of the old building. But it needs a farm, and the need will become acute if at a later stage it finds itself producing more chicks than it can sell. Meanwhile, however, it is one of the most truly named "workhouses" in Ireland.

HAYSHEDS AND GRASS SILOS AT DOVEA HOUSE CO-OPERATIVE CREAMERY FARM

CHAPTER XVI

Dovea Co-operative Farm

(1) 1947

THE idea of the local creamery acquiring Dovea House and farm originated in a lecture by Dr. H. Kennedy given in 1944. After the lecture the owner of Dovea House—a typical Big House owned by a far from typical Captain Trant—interviewed Dr. Kennedy and suggested that if he and his wife might live out their term in a wing of the Big House, and the woods and other amenities of the property were preserved, he would be disposed to sell the farm to the Centenary Creamery Society for co-operative cultivation and use.

The latter had the wit and enterprise to take the offer, and the deal was completed on very reasonable financial terms. Dovea Farm had formerly consisted of some 2,000 acres, but had been pruned by the Land Commission for the purpose of creating, at the national expense, the usual 20 to 30 acre "economic" holdings.

The 200 arable acres that were left required more intensive cultivation and management than the owner felt able to provide, if an adequate output was to be secured, hence his very sensible and public-spirited offer. All this happened in 1944.

In Ireland memories are long and the way of the pioneer in social organisation is not easy. About 100 years ago the agent of an ancestor of Captain Trant was shot and a couple of local persons were made amenable and hanged though widely believed innocent. That, of course, was in the bad old days.

Some misguided persons, doubtless exploiting this age-old grievance, thought it would be a good idea to burn the hay belonging to the Co-operative Society, which was situated in a hay-barn at the Big House. Presumably, the object was to convince all concerned that dividing up the 200 acre farm would be a better national policy than cultivating it collectively as proposed.

However, this contretemps was successfully overcome. The members of the Creamery Society provided each a certain amount of hay to replace what was lost, and some silage that had been made on the spot proved an efficient substitute for the time being, thereby convincing the farm manager that silage was good cattle feed—a thing about which he had been doubtful before.

The net effect of all this is that there were in 1947 three separate ménages installed in the Big House premises— Captain and Mrs. Trant, the farm steward, with four of the 16 workers—and a posse of Civic Guards. Apart from all this, relations with the immediate neighbours are most friendly.

When I visited the farm in 1947 there were 40 heifers and 40 bullocks as well as 16 cows on the land—a reasonably high proportion of stock to acreage—but since that date the number of cattle, and especially of cows, has increased substantially. Sixteen workers were in permanent employment in 1946 at a wage of 52/6 per week, plus firewood, plus housing and milk. The money deduction from the wages of those who lived in the Big House was 12/6 weekly.

These perquisites are a substantial addition to the money wage, and the real wage is very much in excess of the standard minimum. An employment density of eight persons to 100 acres of crops and pasture is high for the larger Irish farms, but has since been exceeded here and elsewhere.

In addition to the permanent workers, who live in the Big House (the unmarried ones) or in cottages round about the farm, if they happen to be married, the creamery provides extra manpower at busy times—a kind of shock troops—by switching some of the permanent employees and transporting them for temporary work on the farm—a matter of five or six miles.

The economy of such an arrangement is obvious, especially if one bears in mind that Irish creameries only work to full capacity during the summer months, and have, therefore, surplus workers available during the winter months.

If one asks how this 200 acre farm can support a wage bill which must approximate to £3,000 a year, the answer is capital equipment, co-operative solidarity and good farm management.

The farm had in 1947 two tractors, costing £300 each; a threshing machine, costing £600; two binders, costing £100 each; two two-furrow ploughs, costing £50 each; two disc-harrows, costing £60 each; besides a number of horses and the usual equipment of horse-drawn implements.

Even before buying the farm the creamery had acquired a number of expensive agricultural machines, the use of which was hired out to members.   Having their own farm enabled this service to be extended considerably and provides a convenient centre for storing, marshalling and "servicing" the farm machines.   About 25 per cent of the tractors' time was on hire.

Grass cultivation was and is the primary activity on this farm.   About 10 acres per annum are being re-seeded, while old pasture is being subjected to the traditional treatment with slag and semsol.   The results are being noted and compared.   There is no controversy about the supreme value of a close-growing sward of first-class pasture, but the best way to get that cheapest and best of all animal feeds is still a matter of controversy.   The data then in process of being obtained at Dovea farm illuminated this problem.

Poultry had not yet made an appearance there in 1947. Pigs were in evidence—one boar and six sows providing a possible output of 120 pigs a year.   Ten acres of potatoes were being grown.   A normal yield from this acreage of potatoes, plus surplus skim milk, would go a long way towards feeding 120 pigs.

Dovea Farm is well provided with hay-sheds, and farm buildings.   Within one of the existing hay-sheds a number of concrete silos for grass silage was being constructed.   The idea was to have the advantage of a roof over the silos (rain is bad for silage).   The space between the top of the silos and the roof of the hay-shed was packed with hay in due course.   The weight of the hay helps to compress the silage.

Dovea Farm is not, perhaps, a co-operative farm in the generally accepted sense of that term.   The persons actually working the farm are employees of a co-operative creamery society, consisting of farmers living within a radius of perhaps 5 or 10 miles from the Central Creamery.   The farm employees are not necessarily members of the Co-operative Society.

Nevertheless, their spirit is fully co-operative, and the quality and quantity of their work leave nothing to be desired.

(2) 1948.

The Ballyduff Co-operative Creamery is officially known as the Centenary Creamery because it was founded in 1898. If one is lucky enough to find Mr. O'Mahony on the premises one has reached the fountain-head of information about the creamery and the creamery-owned Dovea Farm. The latter is situated some five miles on the other side of Thurles. The "Centenary" is one of the larger creameries, having a milk supply of some one-and-a-half million gallons. Its total turnover *qua* creamery approximates to £250,000, and consists as to about half of dairy produce sales and as to the other half of sales of "agricultural goods."

In August, 1948, the operative staff on the farm was still sixteen, which is rather a high number for a 200 statute acre farm. But some of the workers are skilled at building and construction, and a high proportion of the time and labour of all was spent on works of permanent improvement. The farm is really equipped and staffed to cultivate a larger acreage than 200. Actually, it was possible to rent 120 additional acres of conacre in the 1948 season.

Since my visit in August, 1947, the number of cows had gone up from 16 to 30, and there were also 35 in-calf heifers, 35 heifers eighteen months old, and about 40 large bullocks. The aim is to keep the maximum number of cows, rear all their progeny, and sell the surplus males as stores or fat. But as a result of intensive cultivation, manuring, re-seeding, and successful preservation of silage by the new A.I.V. process, the feeding capacity of the farm is now such that numerous animals must be bought in for fattening to supplement those it has been possible to rear on the farm. With 160 tons of well made hay and the contents of six silos full of A.I.V., preserved grass it was possible to feed a considerable number of dry stock as well as cows during the winter of 1948/49.

Pig production was being maintained with one boar and four sows. There were, however, six sows there in 1947.

Poultry did not figure at all. There are too many foxes about. This is a serious limiting factor on poultry production in many parts of Ireland, and sooner or later something drastic will have to be done about it on a large scale.

As for crops—there were, in August, 1948, 9 acres under potatoes, 35 under wheat, 10 under oats and 20 under roots, including beet. Much of this tillage was done on the con-acre "take" of 120 acres, but, even so, the number of cows and large dry stock per 100 acres of crops and pasture is very high.

It would be quite impossible to aim at such intensive production had it not been for the success of their experi-ments in re-seeding worn out pastures and preserving grass silage. About a year ago the creamery manager and his colleagues were ploughing up and re-seeding some old pastures while attempting to revive others by the application of suitable artificial manures without ploughing, and were comparing results. They are now convinced that ploughing up and re-seeding is the best. The other method improves the grass, too, but was also said to improve the weeds.

I have observed some of these re-seeded pastures at Dovea and elsewhere and have been much impressed by their appearance. More important still, the local farmers also observe them, and are disposed to imitate them in their own practice.

These creamery-operated farms are of the utmost edu-cational value, precisely because they are run on a commercial basis, and are designed to show that scientific farming is also the most profitable farming. The ordinary farmer is more impressed by a favourable profit and loss account than by demonstrations carried on at the taxpayers' expense. I am glad to notice that Dovea Farm was able to show a net profit on trading account in 1947 of £105 7s. 4d. That was arrived at after charging to a single year seeds, manures, and feeding stuffs, worth £1,837 14s. 7d., much of the value of which can be realised only in the course of four or five years.

As for equipment, in addition to the tractors, etc., in evidence in 1947, they had acquired a grass "pick up" for collecting freshly-cut silage grass in the swathe and a silage elevator for feeding it into the silo when it had reached the farm-yard. Tractor power, harnessed to implements like these, solves the problem of collecting, transporting, and storing

silage grass. The ordinary small farmer is often defeated
by the practical difficulties connected with silage making.
If he is to solve them he must have the use of modern
implements and access to tractor power. The creamery-
owned Dovea Farm demonstrates the machinery in operation
on its own farm and hires it out to the Society's own members
when wanted.

(3) 1949.

Even a casual observer of Irish agricultural phenomena
must realise that we are passing through a veritable
agricultural revolution. Government policy is playing a
significant part in this process, but beneath the surface a
still more significant force has been in operation which is
a salutary example of co-operatively organised private
enterprise.

Within the last decade certain creameries in the south-
western counties acquired farms which they exploit under
expert management in conjunction with their major activities.
One such is Mitchelstown. Drinagh, Milford, Dungarvan
and Kanturk are other notable examples. Here we are
concerned with the further history of Dovea Creamery Farm.

During the war years, when there was an acute scarcity
of expensive labour economising agricultural machinery, this
Creamery Farm hired out to its members the occasional use
of the power machines which it maintained and "serviced."
In 1949 there was no similar scarcity. But there are certain
operations, now in demand on farms of all sizes, which
require not only expert supervision, but specialised machines
which ordinary farmers are not likely to possess. Such
operations are, for example, the production of first-class
grass silage and the re-seeding of old pasture. This
Creamery Farm makes available to its individual members on
their own farms not only the necessary machines, but the
expert supervision without which disappointing results are
apt to be obtained. In this and in other ways it is promoting a more intensive agriculture and a higher output per
man and per acre in all the regions affected by its activities.

The Creamery Manager and farm steward took me round
and showed me, among other livestock, 37 cows and 74
in-calf heifers. It seemed a huge proportion of in-calf

heifers, but, as they explained, many of these heifers would
be sold as springers to their members, and in that way the
quality of the cows kept in the whole neighbourhood was
being graded up.   The farm did not look for any direct
profit from this transaction, but the creamery would benefit
from an increasing milk supply.   This is a solid contribution
to the increase of the real national income—a process in
which all are deeply interested.   Actually, the milk supply
here and elsewhere has been increasing very substantially in
recent years, and this is one of the causes of that very
desirable increase.   In 1948 it exceeded by 150 gallons per
cow the yield obtained in 1945 in this creamery area.

There are about 200 arable acres in the farm in question,
but, to accommodate the increasing stock and the substantial
area of tillage, it was found necessary, as already mentioned,
to take in a conacre letting of 120 statute acres of other
land.   It looks as if the economic unit for the kind of
intensive highly mechanised farming practised on this farm
is much more than 200 acres.   Indeed, the Mitchelstown
farm has also found that its small size cramps its style.
Both farms could operate more economically and more
scientifically if they had about 500 acres each of their own
to use.   In the light of these experiences it seems desirable
that Land Commission policy should be revised.   The whole
economic position of small family farms (which must remain
the prevailing type) would be strengthened if every significant
agricultural area contained at least one large farm operated
on lines similar to these.

The output of the farm consists mainly of milk, cattle,
and pigs, but crop sales account for about 30 per cent of
sales off the farm, and wheat for about two-thirds of crop
sales.   The 37 cows are milked by five men, without a milking
machine.   Altogether, 12 permanent and 6 casual workers
are now employed, which is a high proportion of "persons
occupied" per 100 acres of crops and pasture.   In the
country as a whole the ratio is about 6 persons.   On small
farms it is much higher, but much family labour on very
small farms is notoriously under-employed.

Gross output per acre (including the conacre letting)
appears to be of the order of £30.   This compares very
favourably with the average of £23 6s. 0d. for 296 Northern

Ireland farms which kept accounts in 1947/48. "Net output" would probably exceed £20 per acre. Even if the farm by itself showed no net profit the financial outlook with regard to it need cause no one sleepless nights. What it loses on the swings the creamery—and the country—will gain on the roundabouts, and I don't think it is losing anything on the swings either.

CHAPTER XVII

MITCHELSTOWN CO-OPERATIVE FARM

(1) 1948

THE Mitchelstown Co-operative Agricultural Society, Ltd., was founded in 1919, and had in 1948 a total turnover of well over one million pounds. It organises and focuses the economic life of a fertile valley that stretches for more than a dozen miles between the beautiful Galtee range of mountains on the north and the Knockmealdown Mountains, no less beautiful, on the south. It employs 500 persons of both sexes at the height of the season, and distributes in wages over £62,000 per annum. Its varied activities include a "store," in which it sells all farm requirements as well as groceries and draperies. It also buys wheat and oats from its members, selects and grades the grain, arranges for the milling in Mallow of appropriate amounts, while reserving and preparing suitable qualities for subsequent re-sale to members as seed.

To a certain extent all this co-operative control of agricultural commerce and processing must have cut into the vested interests of local merchants. There is said to be a certain amount of local opposition on that score, but certainly, to the casual observer, Mitchelstown has all the appearance of a prosperous town. An increase of agricultural wealth and purchasing power has never yet brought ruin to local merchants in Ireland. The processes of economic readjustment are always easy when real wealth is increasing. If merchants must have lost trade in some directions they must have gained more than they have lost by expansion in other directions. In that connection the fact that £62,000 in wages are being spent locally every year is not without economic significance.

The practice of "portioning off" daughters is not confined to rural Ireland. Rumour has it that "fortunes" running well into four figures are not unknown among the daughters of the Mitchelstown merchants who are being "ruined" by the co-op. It is to be hoped that the infection of this ruin will spread widely in Ireland and elsewhere.

A salutary social and economic revolution must, in fact, have taken place in the whole Mitchelstown region during the last two decades. The authors of this revolution were by no means revolutionary in their outlook and intent. It all began about twenty years ago, because the Society decided to make cheese as well as butter. About 200 years ago Bishop Berkeley had queried : "Whether it be not wonderful that with such pastures, and so many black cattle, we do not find ourselves in cheese." Although our natural resources have always been ideally suitable for this form of dairying, we were traditionally neither a cheese eating nor a cheese manufacturing people. Prior to 1932 the annual consumption was about 1 lb. per head, mostly imported. The British were then eating much more—also mainly imported.

The Mitchelstown Society have been pioneers in changing all that. The national consumption of cheese amounted to nearly 2 lbs. per head in 1944, and Mitchelstown, though the chief centre of manufacture, was by no means the only one. Lately the domestic demand, though growing, has tended to become saturated, and a disposition existed to seek an export market in Britain for surplus cheese. This had to be resisted by public policy, because butter production was still inadequate for increasing domestic demand, and cheese-making creameries were for a time required to expand butter production rather than cheese production.

Whey is the inevitable bye-product of cheese producton, just as skim milk and buttermilk are bye-products of butter production. Normally, the farmers take home skim milk and feed pigs, poultry, and calves with it. But the output of whey—also useable in pig feeding—was in Mitchelstown more than the farmers were disposed to take home. It became a sewage-disposal problem in the first instance, and treating it as such was neither locally popular nor economically justifiable. So it was decided to acquire a remnant of Kingston Desmesne Farm, amounting to 160 acres, and the farm buildings associated with it, which happily had escaped the conflagration of 1922. Originally the desmesne farm contained 1,100 acres. Unhappily, most of it had been otherwise disposed of before this bright idea occurred to the Society.   As things have turned out, although most intensive use is made of their 160 acres, many desirable developments are impeded because the farm is much too small.

The first step was to establish a suitably housed herd of 2,000 pigs, and to specialise in potato growing on the farm for their sustenance.   Whey formed an important part of their summer ration, and in winter, when the whey supply failed, potatoes were the principal ingredient.   The whey and potatoes fed the pigs, and the sewage from the pig-pens, suitably distributed, nourished the land.   To grow potatoes year after year on the same land is apt to make it potato-sick.   So latterly the tendency has been to curtail potato growing and put increasing emphasis on re-seeding with fresh grass for silage.   Cows and bulls are now of increasing importance on that farm.   About a year ago they were trying out the new form of acid silage known as A.I.V.   The idea has been imported from Finland.   It has been a complete success.   Cows fed on that last winter milked as well as they had done on summer grass and required no ''concentrates'' unless they gave more than three-and-a-half gallons a day. Incidentally, they are now making A.I.V. silage at Dovea and elsewhere with promising results.   It appears to be the answer to the maiden's prayer so far as Irish agriculture is concerned.

The results of re-seeding on land that has been fertilised by pig sewage, and has carried a potato crop before being sown down *without a nurse crop,* have to be seen to be believed.   Even so, some of the facts reported to me by Mr. Roche, the General Manager, would have imposed a strain on my credulity if I had not seen things with my own eyes and known the reliability of my informant.   Forty statute acres were seeded in June, 1947, and cut twice for silage in the next few months, yielding 16 tons to the statute acre.   They were then grazed for a time but rested during the winter months.   On 1st March, 1948, they were grazed again, but the cattle could not keep the pasture down, so it was cut again for silage in May.   This land had carried potatoes for three years before re-seeding.

Thus pigs and cows, potatoes, whey, and grass play their respective parts in the drama of Mitchelstown.   The pig manure—liquid and solid—is of cardinal importance.   I thought a year ago that perfection had been achieved as to the most economic way of distributing this.   But Mr. Roche tells me they are now trying to get a "raining plant" for the more efficient distribution of the liquid manure.

At present there are on the farm two Friesian and one Shorthorn bull, as well as 8 Friesian cows and 35 heifers in process of becoming cows.   The idea is to build up a specialised herd of Friesian cows numbering 150.   That number of cows with ancillary young stock on a farm of 160 statute acres gives one something to think about.   Such a degree of intensity of milch cows *fed exclusively on the produce of the relevant farm* has nowhere else, to my knowledge, been realised in Ireland.

The technique practised on the Mitchelstown Farm is equally available, with suitable modifications, on any farm in Ireland.   All that is needed to bring about a vast increase of production by this method is the wit, the enterprise, the finance, and the readiness to apply scientific knowledge, which are, unfortunately, not universally in evidence. However, where Mitchelstown has pioneered the way doubt- less many others will follow—in fact, are following.   There is much to be said for the herd instinct when the leadership of the herd is good.

(2) 1949.

Up till 1922 the most prominent object in the neighbour- hood of Mitchelstown was the castle—the ancestral seat of the Kingston family—but it went up in smoke in 1922.   The Demesne Farm of some 1,100 acres was subsequently divided up by the Land Commission into small holdings in accord- ance with what is now traditional policy.   However, a remnant of about 160 statute acres remained, and this, as we have seen, was acquired by the creamery in 1942.   The immediate object was to find an outlet for the whey, which is a bye-product of cheese manufacture.   Large modern piggeries were erected, and the whey has since been used as a principal element in the ration of the thousands of pigs which are produced and maintained therein.

In the war years meals were scarce and it was necessary to cultivate scores of acres of potatoes on the farm in order

to provide a complete ration for the pigs. The pig manure
was used to fertilise the potato crop and phenomenal yields
were obtained. But after a few years it became obvious
that to go on growing potatoes in large quantities, even on
so large a farm, would make the land "potato-sick" and
invite trouble.

When the war came to an end meals become more
plentiful, and it became possible as well as desirable to ease
off potato growing and switch over to the intensive cultivation
of grass and clovers for pasture, hay, and silage, but prin-
cipally for pasture and silage. Even the pigs are important
consumers of grass, which is cut and fed to them in the
piggeries. About one-fourth of their ration in terms of
food units can consist of this highly succulent fodder.

The problem of getting pig manure back to the land in
connection with a potato-growing programme is no different
from that found by the ordinary farmer everywhere, though
probably few farmers had such efficient means of utilising
the liquid manure of pigs for potato growing as what were
in use in Mitchelstown during the potato era.

Last year, when grass was becoming the principal crop
on the farm, it was decided to acquire a "raining plant"
for liquid manure. This has been in operation all this
season; the technique used (and the results achieved) must
command the admiration of the visitor. The liquid manure
is collected in a tank at the highest point of the farm, and
even the solid manure is brought in a semi-liquid form to
this tank for convenience of handling. There is a series of
pipes, easily connected and disconnected, running from an
electric pump to wherever the raining plant is for the time
situated. When the pump is switched on the plant proceeds
to revolve and sprinkle a circle with a radius of about
30 yards. When this area has had enough of the fertilising
fluid the pump is stopped, another pipe or two is connected
on, and the process begins all over again on a fresh circle
farther down the field.

When I was there, in September, 1949, I saw a third
cutting of highly nutritious grass being taken off a field of
new grass which had already yielded two cuttings that year
for silage making.

The only crop now grown is grass—in its various species.
Wheat, oats, and potatoes are a thing of the past on that

farm. This new grass economy is certainly not synonymous with the rancher economy, about which so much has been heard in the past. The farm employs 15 workers, all equipped with the most modern labour-saving machinery, as well as 10 workers whose special job is looking after the pigs.

A pig which is fed on meals alone will consume about 8 lbs. a day. This is the most expensive part of the ration; with meals costing about 20 shillings a cwt., a pig will eat about £7 worth during its short life. If the bonham costs the farmer £5 or £6, the farmer will be doing well if he has £3 10s. 0d. for himself by the time he has been paid for the fat pig.

On the Mitchelstown Farm it is possible to cut down the meal ration to 2 lbs. a day, the rest consisting of whey and grass. Even so, it buys about 200 tons of meals in the year, an annual expenditure of £4,000. That corresponds to an output of 2,500 pigs in the year, but capacity is being rapidly expanded and will soon reach the 5,000 pig mark. The breeding stock now consists of 180 sows and 5 boars, but in addition large numbers of bonhams are bought in from the Society's members, and this gives an element of flexibility to its output.

The turnover of the farm was £19,000 in 1942, and is now of the order of £40,000.

However, pigs are not the only animals on the farm. There are at present 24 Friesian cows and 30 in-calf heifers as well as numerous calves and 8 bulls. The object is to reach a point at which the farm will carry one cow to the statute acre, and supply that cow with all the sustenance she needs for giving up to $3\frac{1}{2}$ gallons of milk per day. As we have seen it has been found that cows fed on the A.I.V. silage, which the farm produces, require no concentrates in the winter-time unless they are giving more than $3\frac{1}{2}$ gallons of milk per day.

The farm also functions as an artificial insemination centre for cattle. The bulls (four Shorthorn, three Friesian and one Hereford) have been instrumental in fertilising 2,000 cows in the present season. This is the best means yet devised for grading up the quality of the milking stock kept on farms generally.

The farm has had to go in for an exclusively grass-growing programme because it is much too small. If it consisted of

500 acres instead of only 160 it could practise a more normal rotation, with corn, root and/or green crops playing a prominent part.   This would facilitate getting the more solid cattle manure back to the land and mixed with the soil. Like similar farms elsewhere, its style is cramped because the area it cultivates is not large enough to constitute a fully economic unit for large-scale intensive farming, involving the use of scientific knowledge and modern technique.

One cannot help regretting that Land Commission policy left it only a remnant of 160 acres to acquire in 1942 out of a Demesne Farm of originally 1,100 acres.   The country needs many Mitchelstown Creamery Farms, and perhaps it is not heresy to suggest that it is quite time land tenure legislation and Land Commission policy were revised, so as to facilitate their emergence and enable them to achieve their optimum results.

CHAPTER XVIII

The Outlook in 1950

IRISH agriculture, at all events that of the Twenty-six Counties, has had a notoriously difficult time during the last two decades. The immediate prospect is fair enough but there is a lot of leeway to make up.

The world depression of 1929–1931 did our agriculture no real harm, but the Economic War of 1932–1938 was a severe body blow, and the outbreak of the second World War prevented it from effecting the recovery which the settlement of the Economic War otherwise made possible.

Northern Ireland not only escaped the Economic War but profited by the various British agricultural policies which began to be carried out in the 1930's. Their subsequent intensification under the stress of war brought important financial gains to Northern agriculture which we could not share.

The extent of the leeway we now have to recover can best be measured by a comparison of our agricultural record in the last two decades with that of Northern Ireland. The comparison is fair enough, because, so far as climate and natural resources are concerned, we have, if anything, the advantage, and the pattern of Northern agricultural objectives tends to be very much the same as ours.

According to official publications, the index number of the volume of our agricultural output was in 1938–39 97·0 as compared with 1929–30 (100). In 1937–38 the index number of Northern Ireland agricultural output was 132 as compared with 1927–29 (100).

During the second World War the pattern of our agricultural output was perforce violently disturbed a second time. The volume also suffered. According to the *Irish Trade Journal* of June, 1950 (p. 104), the index numbers of the volume of our gross agricultural output (based on 1938–39 = 100) were as follows :—

1938–39	39–40	40–41	41–42	42–43	43–44	44–45	45	46	47	48	49
100	102·8	95·3	98·0	91·7	90·5	92·6	97·6	95·7	89·9	91·9	98·7

In the case of Northern Ireland the pattern of production was also violently disturbed by the second World War and volume also suffered. Between 1942 and 1945 the reduction was of the order of 7 per cent (compared to 1937–39), and by 1946/47 more than 100 per cent of pre-war output had been obtained. In view of the fact that the availability of fertilisers increased from some 40,000 tons in 1939 in their case to 200,000 in 1947, while hardly any fertilisers were available down here, the performance of our agriculture bears favourable comparison with that of Northern Ireland during the second World War period.

The real handicap still suffered by our agriculture was the failure to increase output by more than 30 per cent, as Northern Ireland did, during the period ending in 1938. If we had done that, and maintained a uniform volume of output during the second World War, our agricultural income would now be some £30 millions more than it is (at present prices) and our national income nearly £100 million greater. This is the handicap which we must overcome before our agricultural achievement can be said to have reached parity with that of Northern Ireland, and meanwhile agricultural progress in that area has not come to an end.

Putting the matter in another way—it appears from official figures that gross output per acre of crops and pasture in Northern Ireland was £5 in 1931–32, £6 10s. 0d. in 1937–38, and £16 0s. 0d. in 1946–47. In our area gross output per acre was in 1929–30 £6 3s. 0d., in 1937–38 £5 0s. 0d., and in 1947 £11 6s. 0d. in terms of current prices.

This calculation is based on an acreage of 2½ millions of crops and pastures in Northern Ireland and 10 millions in our area, which perhaps exaggerates the available area up there and underestimates it down here.

We have not yet lived down the consequences of the Economic War; but it would be unprofitable to rattle those old bones. For financial reasons the import of fertilisers was curtailed during those years. During the more recent war years it was impossible to get them. As compared with a normal pre-Economic War import of some 200,000 tons per annum we imported in 1941 11,000 tons, in 1942 2,000 tons, in 1943 25,000 tons, in 1944 37,000 tons, and in 1945 22,000 tons. If the rate of application which we were practising in 1929-30 had been sustained in every succeeding year it has been calculated that in 1945 our land would have received 2 million tons more phosphate than it actually did receive in the intervening period.   This is the statistical evidence for the existence of a condition of aphosphorosis in our land which in recent years has impaired the fertility and even threatened the lives of our cattle.   The Fianna Fail Government was by no means entirely to blame for the impossibility of importing phosphates during the second World War (Mr. Churchill and Adolf Hitler must take their share), but Mr. Dillon picturesquely credits the former Government with having evolved a variety of grass that would fill a cow's stomach and yet let her die of starvation where she stood, "for that is the correct description of aphosphorosis."

In view of the extreme scarcity of fertilisers during the second World War it was a magnificent achievement for our agriculture to have maintained the level of output it did maintain.   The agriculture of Northern Ireland did not do much better, and it is on official record that it could not have done what it did but for the fact that "the availability of fertilisers increased from thirty or forty thousand tons in 1939 to 200,000 tons in 1947."

The recent substantial increase in the quantity of fertilisers imported here will have, in fact has had, the most dramatic effect in restoring the fertility of our land and increasing agricultural output.   In 1946 we imported 100,000 tons, in 1947 120,000 tons, in 1948 221,000 tons, and in 1949 259,000 tons.

Already the number of cattle is increasing—heifers in calf from 120,000 in January, 1948, to 158,000 in January, 1949.   Pigs have increased in number by 45 per cent. Exports of poultry, eggs and condensed milk have rapidly increased, and bacon and butter have once more appeared on the export market.   In 1947 580,000 acres of wheat yielded 313,000 tons.   In 1948 a smaller acreage (518,000) yielded a much larger crop (409,000 tons).   In the first four months of 1947 the creameries produced 36,000 cwt. of butter, in the same period of 1948 40,000 cwt., in that of 1949 70,000 cwt.   The trend is now obviously upward, and the prospects are that it will increase in momentum, always assuming that the possible effect of devaluation in increasing our costs will be more than counterbalanced by the expansion of our export opportunities.

The new Government has wholeheartedly adopted the recommendation of the Post-Emergency Committee on Agricultural Policy in favour of ley farming and the cultivation of highly productive strains of grass as our principal crop. In all fairness, it should be stressed that that Committee was set up by the former Government, which was also in process of implementing its principal recommendations when it went out of office.

Under the Marshall Aid Scheme a sum of £40,000,000 in "counterpart" funds became available, and our Government has decided to invest it in the most ambitious project for improving and reclaiming four million acres of potentially fertile Irish land that has yet been undertaken. Two procedures are contemplated. Either the farmer may, from his own resources carry out an approved programme of reclamation, in which case he will receive a grant amounting to two-thirds of the cost, portion of which will, where necessary, take the form of a supply of ground limestone and/or fertilisers for application to the land reclaimed. Alternatively, he can have the work done by a State-created Land Project Organisation. In this case the State will contribute three-fifths of the cost and the farmer two-fifths, "subject to an overriding maximum of £12 per acre." If he cannot pay cash for his share he can repay by way of annuity "calculated on the basis of $3\frac{1}{2}$ per cent interest and $\frac{1}{2}$ per cent sinking fund." If this scheme succeeds it will add four million acres to our effective agricultural area. The gross output from such an additional acreage might well amount to £20,000,000 *a year*. On any reasonable assumptions this is likely to prove a remunerative investment for £40,000,000 of capital from a national as well as an individual point of view.

There have been Farm Improvement Schemes before, but they were vitiated by excessive emphasis on "labour content." The employment given by such schemes is apt to dry up as soon as the funds charitably made available are exhausted. This scheme is based on the principle that anything which increases the productiveness of our soil and the real income of our farmers will be a permanent and expanding source of additional employment and increasing wealth—not only for agricultural producers, but in the economy as a whole. Accordingly, the labour employed on the Land Reclamation Scheme is equipped with every modern mechanical power-operated device for making the most economical use of available labour.   Drag-line excavators, field drain-cutting machines, mole drainers and, of course, bulldozers (e.g. for cleaning scrub), all play a dramatic part.   A bulldozer with crawler tractor costs about £3,000, but there is a liberal provision of loans and grants which will enable mechanically minded enterprising young men to set up as contractors and do a good job for themselves as well as for their neighbours in furtherance of this scheme.

According to a statement which appeared in the public press, the Government's Land Reclamation Scheme has aroused keen interest on the part of the farming community. Before August 26th, 1950, 49,000 applications for the necessary forms had been received by the Department of Agriculture, and more than 44,000 completed forms had been returned.   Work in connection with the scheme was proceeding in every county.   An area of 490,000 acres, formerly useless by reason of defective drainage or other causes, was being rehabilitated.   The work was said to have created a great spirit of co-operation among farmers, local authorities and contractors under the leadership of the Department of Agriculture.

The indirect effect of all this in intensifying the mechanisation of our agriculture as a whole is bound to be considerable.   The numbers of tractors in this area has increased considerably since the war, but the total is only about 12,000, much the same as in Northern Ireland.

The co-operative ownership of such machines is also facilitated in the new legislation.   It is to be hoped that these machines will be co-operatively owned in many cases. In that case the technical revolution in agricultural methods which is now impending will have most interesting and salutary repercussions in the field of social organisation and personal economic relations.

The Outlook in 1951.

But for the weather 1950 would have been a good year for Irish agriculture.   The almost continuous rain since early in July made thousands of acres of hay practically useless for feed. Wheat, barley and oats, which are still grown in considerable quantities, suffered, too, but less seriously. The reason probably is that by reason of the more generous application of varieties of artificial manure—long unavailable or unused—the straw was stronger and there was less "lodging" than might have been expected. There are 12,000 tractors in Éire, much the same number as in Northern Ireland, and therefore relatively much less. But tractor power and modern implements are now much more widely used in Éire than formerly, and they have made possible in this season the saving of harvests that would otherwise have been lost. It is safe to assume that available tractors and implements have been lent or hired for use on neighbours' fields when not required by their proprietors.

The bad hay crop is, of course, a disaster. But if the lesson is duly learnt it may be a blessing in disguise. About fifty years ago the German observer, Dr. Bonn, wrote that the Irish agricultural question is primarily a "turnip" question. At the best, hay is an inadequate feed for dairy and fattening stock in the depth of winter. The cattle dry up and "go back" with such incomplete nourishment. So true is this that another authority once said that the Irish farmer feeds his livestock in the winter on the most expensive of all rations—beefsteak from their own bodies. Dr. Bonn recommended turnips as a supplementary ration, which provided also the succulence of grass. Nowadays turnips are going out of fashion and silage is coming in. The labour cost of producing turnips is too great, and, anyhow, they have not the protein equivalent of silage well made from young grass.

This season's weather has been effective propaganda in favour of silage making and thousands of farmers are taking the hint, which is also a specific recommendation of the Department of Agriculture. If the practice is not universal, one reason is that there are more than 150,000 farmers whose holdings do not exceed 30 acres in size. Hitherto it has been usual to build concrete silos which, of course, cost money as well as labour. This year even large farmers have been digging suitably drained pit silos on sloping ground. Tractors with a digging attachment can be used for this purpose, but in any case a silo can be dug out with a spade, and the principal cost is labour and "elbow grease." However, that is not the only problem for the small farmer. To get the right kind of young grass it is often necessary to plough up and re-seed old pastures. You can make a good job of this if you have the use of a tractor, a disc-harrow, and a Cambridge roller. There is nothing like an adequate supply of these available, particularly of Cambridge rollers.

The filling of a silo is a slow and laborious task if you have to depend on horsepower and manpower. With a "buck-rake" and hydraulic lift attached to a tractor it can be done with all convenient ease and speed. All this implies mechanisation, and again the large farmer, or the small farmer, who has access to mechanised power implements, is at an advantage.

Present economic conditions and recent economic experience undoubtedly favour the large farmer and handicap the isolated smallholder. In the years of scarcity the price of wheat had to be raised high enough to make it profitable for the high-cost ill-equipped small farmer to grow it, often on unsuitable land. This conveyed an automatic bonus of additional profit to the large farmers. The price of wheat is still high, and much wheat is still being grown, but not much by the numerous class of small farmers in "Éire." The fact is that low-cost production of tillage crops is only possible on large units of land where every kind of modern labour economising power-driven implement is available. To provide a single tractor and a complete range of tractor driven implements would cost more than £1,000. It would be utterly uneconomic even for the 100-acre farmer to invest so much money in implements for his own exclusive use. The common-sense solution is for farmers, big and small, to get together and dovetail their requirements and specialised activities to one another's needs with reference to a combined acreage of 1,000 acres or more in each case. The traditional system of lending implements and services would be regularised and extended. With an agreed tariff for the various exchanges, such a body of closely integrated farmers would function very much like a cheque-clearing union in a banking system, and only balances would need to be settled in cash.

The country cannot afford the high production costs of her numerous ill-equipped small farmers, for they are a material factor in the present high cost of living for our urban population as well as a handicap in our competition for export trade.

Mechanisation alone will make possible the maintenance of a large area under tillage and the payment of greatly enhanced agricultural wages, which are still much below Northern Irish and British standards. More mechanisation does not mean less grass, though it should mean a smaller area under permanent pasture. By means of mechanisation and suitable manuring the stock-carrying capacity of our pasture land can be doubled or trebled. As we have seen, it is also almost an essential of efficient silage making.

More mechanisation also means more employment per 100 acres of crops and pasture. The average number of persons occupied per 100 acres of crops and pasture is less than two on farms exceeding 200 acres in size. On many farms of 200 acres and more *which are highly mechanised* and fully equipped the density of employment per 100 acres is at least three times as great. To bring the average density of employment up to the level of six per 100 acres would require nearly 200,000 additional agricultural workers. At the moment they are simply not there in the more fertile eastern counties. But, as Mr. Freeman has shown,[1] there are more than 12 persons looking for work on each 100 acres of crops and pastures in the congested west—and not finding it *there*

Will the owners of large farms in the midlands revert to a mainly grass economy now that tillage is no longer compulsory? It depends partly on whether they can continue to count on buying in enough two-year-old dry cattle that have been born and reared in the dairying south-western counties. If this stream of young cattle diminished or dried up the midland farmers would have to rear their own cattle, and that means tillage and, of course, more mechanisation. Calves and yearling cattle won't thrive on a winter ration of hay and grass alone. Some of the best farmers in the midlands are already rearing their own young Hereford

[1] *Ireland*, p. 198.

stock, and they prefer them to the surplus progeny of the Limerick "dual purpose" cow.

There is a tendency in the dairying counties to abandon the dual purpose Dairy Shorthorn in favour of the Friesian. The surplus progeny of the latter breed will have to be knocked on the head at birth, for the midland farmers have no use for them as beef animals. More Friesians in the south-west will increase the flow of milk to the creameries and intensify the problem of finding an economic outlet for surplus butter—already very acute.

The dairying industry has been subsidised by the general taxpayer ever since the early 1930's on the ground that it was a pivotal element in our whole agricultural economy. So it was; but only so long as the midland farmer depended for his raw material on the surplus progeny of cows in the dairying counties. Hitherto the taxpayer has cheerfully contributed an amount which must now aggregate more than £20 millions to enhance the price received by the creamery supplying farmers. In 1947–48 the estimate for this purpose was £2,065,000. In 1948–49 £2,375,000 was required, and there seems no limit to its possibe increase. The creamery suppliers have become so accustomed to the taxpayers' bounty that they look on it now as a sacred right.

The case for the subsidy, already very weak, will completely disappear if the dairy farmers abandon the dual purpose cow. But it might be a good thing for the country if the "graziers" of the midlands had to rear more of their own young cattle.

Gross agricultural output in 1949 was 98·7 per cent of pre-war in volume. In 1947 it had been 89·9, and in 1948 91·9. The increase was general—more cattle, more pigs, more poultry, more eggs. Cattle numbers still continue to increase, but latterly the price obtainable for eggs and pigs has tended downwards, while the cost of imported feed has increased. Indian meal at 30/– a cwt. makes it difficult to expand egg and pig production without incurring a loss. Recently published figures suggest that the upward trend of poultry and pig population has been checked. If it is not to be reversed, our farmers must find some cheaper raw material than Indian meal at 30/– a cwt. Ymer barley, widely grown in Ireland this year, may possibly be the solution. The harvesting of it has been no easy matter.

CHAPTER XIX

THE LOCAL INTEGRATION OF AGRICULTURAL PRODUCTION

THE establishment of a system of peasant proprietorship in Ireland left many problems unsolved. Rural depopulation has proceeded apace, and has not been confined to the regions of poorest soil. Output per man and per acre has increased only slowly, and the wide margin of difference between the results obtained by the best farmers and the worst, in otherwise similar conditions, suggests that many, if not most, farmers are very indifferent stewards of their share of the national resources. The social justification for the principle of private property in land is that private property promotes private enterprise, and that society as a whole is the gainer from the spontaneous initiative of numerous profit-making private owners of land.

If for various reasons many landed proprietors, big and small, display no initiative and obtain from their farms only a fraction of the output that it should be possible to obtain, the community as a whole cannot remain indifferent, and a problem of social statesmanship is created. Some would have us abolish the institution of private property in land in favour of its social ownership. That, by the way, was the policy urged by Michael Davitt, James Fintan Lalor, and James Connolly, but this particular part of their doctrine is forgotten or ignored.

For centuries the land of Ireland was the prize as well as the battleground of successive waves of "land thieves," to use James Connolly's unflattering expression. There was a series of confiscations, in which the power of the State was used, not to abolish private property in land, but to transfer it from one set of private proprietors to another.

Perhaps this very experience has deprived the institution of private property of much of its social value. For landowners, aware of how they had acquired their title, could feel no certainty that they would not be displaced by another successful wave of land appropriators. Hence they tended

M

to use their land as a means of acquiring an easy income and
leading a lazy life. This was intelligible enough in the case
of the Cromwellian landowners. Even to-day there are
30-acre landlords who let their land for a rack-rent, and
work at other occupations.

The days of large-scale confiscations, replacing one set of
large-scale proprietors by another, have indeed passed. But
the acquisition of land for private ownership, by the help
of the State, is now in some cases the result of success in
domestic politics. The tendency is to emphasise the
acquisition of land for private ownership as a suitable
reward for national services, and to ignore the social
obligations the recognition of which alone justifies the
institution of private property in land. The "rancher"
class is not the only one which fails to recognise these
obligations. It is no solution of the problem of congestion,
or of low output per man and per acre, to replace 500-acre
ranchers by 30-acre ranchers. Indeed, the problem is
insoluble on these lines. For there simply is not enough
land to go round if every "congest" and landless man is to
be provided with an "economic" 30-acre holding, which in
fact would be most uneconomic if there was nothing but
30-acre holdings throughout the country.

The game of "beggar-my-neighbour," which proceeded
for so many centuries in the history of Irish land tenure,
has undermined the sense of security which is an essential
element in the concept of private land ownership, and
deprived that institution of much of its potential social value.
The rural mind is hag-ridden by the ghosts of an unfortunate
past.

James Connolly wrote a book called "Labour in Irish
History," the main contention of which was that "capitalist"
ideas about the sanctity of private property and the right to
private profit-making are in fact a foreign import which
came with the Conquest, and are alien to the Gaelic mind.
The communal cultivation of land was a characteristic
feature of the old Gaelic social order, and ultimately ownership belonged to no individual but to the clan or sept.

Dr. E. E. Evans, of Queen's University, Belfast, in his
book "Irish Heritage" finds traces of former communal
land tenures in the "rundale" system, and in the clusters
of "clachans" of peasant houses which are still found in

parts of Donegal and Connaught. The completely isolated farms of to-day are, in his view, a comparatively modern innovation. The "townlands" which still survive originally contained such clusters of houses, referred to as "towns." "These self-sufficing communities were held together by blood ties and by the exchange of services under the Irish open-field or 'rundale' system of cultivation" (p. 50, *op. cit.*).

If James Connolly and Dr. Evans are right it would appear that an important part of the Conquest still remains to be undone. For the "foreign" idea of the sanctity of private property, in land and other means of production, appears to have penetrated deeply into the Irish mind.

The co-operative movement set out to remedy the defects inherent in the dispersal of agricultural effort in a multitude of isolated small holdings. It has achieved only a qualified success, mainly in the south-western counties, where the prevalent type of farm contains from 50 to 100 acres. It has made no material contribution to the alleviation of the circumstance that the smallest farms are in general found on the poorest soil, notably in Connaught and Donegal.

Co-operative processing and co-operative buying and selling do not appeal to the imagination or create a sense of social solidarity with an emotional content. Co-operation, in the literal sense of working together in the daily and seasonal tasks of husbandry, survives as a traditional custom, but has not yet been consciously organised and placed on a common-sense footing.

Modern conditions of mechanised husbandry have out-moded the small 30 acre farm as an economic unit. If tillage is to expand and the cereal raw materials of the specialised animal husbandry, which alone is appropriate to the small holding, are to be made available to the latter at an economic price, then tillage must be envisaged with reference to 500 acre or 1,000 acre units. Only with reference to such units is it possible and economic to have not only the tractor power, but the great variety of expensive implements which enable maximum use to be made of available power, and in any case are essential for efficient cultivation and land improvement.

Failure to solve the problem thus presented will mean either a decline in tillage and a consequent low output per acre, with rural depopulation, or the concentration of economic power in the hands of individuals who can afford to own these expensive machines. If they choose to exercise this power in accordance with the worst traditions of capitalism, they could bring all their poorer neighbours into virtual economic servitude, whether the latter continue to be legally the owners of small holdings or not.

The task of the social architect is to create a system of social organisation which will enable maximum use to be made of modern mechanised methods and scientific knowledge, in an environment which preserves the economic freedom of all and creates an atmosphere of mutual helpfulness and goodwill.

Some valuable suggestions with a view to this end were made by Senator Richards Orpen in a paper on "Post-War Planning in Irish Agriculture," which concluded a series of articles by different authors in the "Irish Independent" in 1943. He advocates a system of what he calls "Economic Farm Units," each one serving a region of some 1,500 acres.

In a paper read by the present writer to the Statistical and Social Inquiry Society of Ireland, on 27th November, 1947, his suggestions were adopted with some modifications.

It will be convenient at this stage to quote at length from the paper referred to.

The variety of our climate, soil, and geographical conditions is such that probably no two "Economic Farm Units" or Co-operative Farming Societies would be identical in function and activities. A working example already exists. The Mitchelstown Creamery exploits a farm of 160 acres at Mitchelstown in connection with its cheese factory. It maintains a large pool of agricultural machinery, not only for use on the collective farm but for hiring out to its members for use in their own farms. It grinds corn for the members, and maintains a store in which it sells agricultural requisites. Its total turnover now exceeds £1 million per annum, and it is undoubtedly the dominant factor in the prosperity of the rural community within a radius of five or ten miles.

For the maximum development of the possibilities inherent in this movement, it is desirable that the collective farm should be conveniently near the creamery which owns it. Unfortunately in some cases they are some miles apart. It is also desirable that a big house or mansion should be available on the farm to accommodate the farm manager and the celibate working staff. Life in common is in itself a valuable education. Given suitable residential accommodation, such farms could in some cases become perhaps high schools, analogous to the Danish Folk Schools. A floating population of young farmers could thus pass through them and return to their respective neighbourhoods with their vision enlarged, their imagination quickened, and their sympathies deepened.

The Mitchelstown Farm has no mansion on it. The former abode of the Earls of Kingston did not survive till our day.

This limits its possibilities of development in the cultural and educational sense, which is so highly desirable. But such as it is, it may be regarded, at least in the economic sense, as a good working model of the kind of "Economic Farm Unit" which Captain Orpen envisages for every appropriate centre in our heterogeneous agricultural regions. Needless to say, if our agriculture were fully organised on these lines, there would be as much variety in the functions and activities of the various Economic Farm Units as there is variety in the character of our agricultural resources and in the geographical and human conditions of the various areas. Making allowance for this, the general picture may be given in Captain Orpen's own words :—

"The method which looks most promising as regards this country may be called the 'Economic Farm Unit.' I propose to describe this system in some detail, as it has features of interest peculiar in itself. The Unit is composed of a centre and subsidiary parts, and the area may be anything from one thousand to twenty thousand acres, depending on local circumstances.

"First let us take the Centre. This may be a large farm or a group of smaller farms willing to co-operate with one another, or it may in certain cases be a central processing organisation according to the farming practised in the area. We will consider first the Centre in a tillage area where the chief cash crop is grain. The Centre will have the necessary equipment for growing and handling grain in bulk, tractors, tillage, harvesting and threshing implements (or 'Combines' and grain dryers). The Centre will be able to produce grain far cheaper and with greater certainty than the small farmer, or Subsidiary, with inadequate equipment and everything against him except an excess of unpaid family labour. The Centre will not be handicapped as the larger farmer is to-day, because it can call on the excess labour on the Subsidiary Farms to assist in the harvest.

"Turning to the Subsidiary Farm, grain may be grown economically on some of these, and the equipment available at the Centre be used to help out the Subsidiary's operations. Other Subsidiaries, who have hitherto wasted their land and strength in producing grain crops uneconomically, can turn to more remunerative occupations because they can now buy their requirements of grain at ex-farm prices within the Unit. We must remember that in the past the subsistence farmer could buy relatively little, as he produced next to nothing for exchange. Now, too, the Subsidiary could devote his activities to production of young stock, dairy, fruit, vegetables, poultry and eggs, bees and flowers. He has a market at his door, as the Unit either processes the produce or distributes it to the consuming area or to factories. The Unit can provide rapid transport to the town and railhead, and at the same time draw farm requirements for distribution to the Subsidiaries. In this type of set-up of, say, fifteen thousand acres, no farmer is more than two and a half miles, as the crow flies, from the Centre, the conveyance of goods and produce by the Subsidiary is no longer an excessive burden, and yet the produce from an Economic Farm Unit of this size would warrant efficient transport facilities, provided as part of the equipment of the Unit.

"The Centre would purchase in bulk much of the requirements of the Subsidiaries at present bought piecemeal, and would provide seed correctly dried and stored, manures, etc. Technical services and advice would form part of the duties of the Centre, as a region of fifteen thousand acres can afford to carry expert technicians quite beyond the means of even the largest farms. Repair work hitherto sent away could now be done on the spot.

"The Centre would process all produce bought in from the Subsidiaries, and as far as possible distribute it in a condition ready for the consumer. Thus the Centre would give employment to many persons who for various reasons were unsuited to field work, and who previously migrated from the countryside, thereby breaking up the family, and causing that serious social and economic phenomenon, the 'flight to the town.' Farm grouping on the lines indicated would tend to a more varied life in rural areas.''

The "Economic Farm Unit" would be a legal personality, representing a close co-operative association of a nucleus of workers, under expert leadership, and a looser federation with all the independently-owned farms in the neighbour-hood. The latter are called by Captain Orpen "Subsidiary Farms," but the term is perhaps misleading. Legally they would be just as independent as the members of any farmers' co-operative society now are. The essential difference would be that the latter could now concentrate their whole energies on production in their own farms, and on extending their productive efforts in new, desirable directions, since all their commercial and processing, and most of their transport problems, would be taken care of by the "Economic Farm Unit." The latter would cultivate the central farm, which might well contain from 500 to 1,000 acres, using all the most modern labour-economising devices and implements. It would maintain a surplus of tractor-power and agricul-tural machines, and skilled personnel to service them. These would be available to supplement the deficiencies of neighbouring farmer members occupying an area of perhaps 15,000 to 20,000 acres. The manpower of the whole area would be strategically mobilisable at a moment's notice. At times, surplus labour from farm members' families would work in the central farm, to meet a temporary seasonal need, or in the various works of long-term improvement on which labour in slack seasons is always usefully occupied in a really progressive farm. At other times labour from farm members' families would follow the machines and skilled personnel of the Economic Farm Unit around to work on the farms of farmer members. In fact they would go on doing very much what they do at present in the threshing season, only it would be done in a fully-organised, com-prehensive manner, and would touch many other useful activities besides threshing. The mutual helpfulness of neighbouring farmers, small, medium, and large, is one of the pleasantest features of Irish rural life. The fact that it does exist, in an informal, unorganised way, is, I think, definite proof that the typical Irish farmer is not an incurably isolationist individualist. All that is necessary, if we are to create a brave new world in the Irish countryside, is to build intelligently and imaginatively on this most happy fact of Irish human nature.

Once the Economic Farm Unit got going in any neighbourhood the activities taking place on the various farms round about would be modified and suitably adjusted. The central farm would doubtless maintain a pig-breeding establishment. Just as at Mitchelstown, it could arrange for finishing some thousands of pigs in the most economic manner. Many of these it would doubtless rear on its own premises. But also, as at Mitchelstown, it would buy in bonhams reared by the members. The latter would thus tend to specialise in the rearing of bonhams rather than the finishing of pigs. Similarly, the individual farm members could specialise in rearing young cattle, passing them on to the central farm at a suitable age. Horticulture and fruit growing would be encouraged, for the central farm would maintain expensive spraying apparatus, and undertake the processing (by quick freeze and other appropriate methods) of members' vegetables and fruit. There would, in fact, be a continuous nexus of reciprocal exchanges between members and the Economic Farm Unit. Labour services and the hire of machinery would figure in these exchanges, as well as the buying of agricultural requisites from the central store, and the sale of agricultural produce to the Economic Farm Unit. No money need pass with every act of exchange. All that would be necessary would be a record of each transaction and an understanding about its price. It would be a strange thing (once the system was fully developed) if at the end of a quarter or a year the central organisation did not owe its members in most cases substantial amounts. These would be drawn on as required by individual family circumstances. In fact, the central organisation would function as an automatic savings bank for its members as well as being their commercial and processing agency.

If one could imagine some hundreds of such farm units operating in every agricultural area in Éire (saturation point would be reached with, perhaps, not more than 400 or 500 such centres) there would remain no problem of agricultural credit for the individual farmer.

The State could if necessary finance the Economic Farm

Units through the Agricultural Credit Corporation. Initially, finance from this source would certainly be needed in every area where there was no financially-strong co-operative creamery to undertake this function. But once the system got under way, and showed promise of success, the ordinary commercial banks would be only too glad to provide any additional finance that might be necessary. The rate at which they could afford to lend to such an organisation would compare very favourably with the rate they require from the ordinary farmer borrower. Given good management and a healthy co-operative spirit, the risk to the bank making a loan to the Economic Farm Unit would be quite negligible.

By methods such as these an intensification and diversification of agricultural production could be stimulated widely. The high standard of production already attained in some of our well-run large-scale *privately* owned farms reflects itself in a high density of employment per 100 acres and in *increasing* local rural population.

The Department of Statistics has supplied me with statistics of population for certain D.E.D.'s, where I happen to know that large-scale farming has been intensively carried on for some time. I give them, but not under their names, as I do not wish to reveal the identity of the farms concerned.

TABLE XIX.

Population Statistics in certain D.E.D.'s.

	A			B			C		
	Total	Males	Females	Total	Males	Females	Total	Males	Females
1871	462	262	200	449	242	207	727	367	360
1881	437	228	209	375	206	169	672	333	339
1891	379	192	187	351	175	176	590	307	283
1901	362	178	184	309	168	141	572	287	285
1911	328	164	164	329	179	150	534	267	267
1926	347	166	181	378	199	179	505	264	241
1936	385	201	184	386	207	179	506	255	251
1946	459	243	216	406	218	188	528	257	271

It would be interesting to make a note of all the rural D.E.D.'s in which population *has* increased in recent decades (there are not so many of them), and then go round the country and find out locally *why* this exceptional pheno- menon has taken place.   Doubtless in many cases, as in those listed above, the answer would be good intensive agricultural production in large, medium or small farms in the D.E.D.'s in question.

From 5 to 10 persons or more per hundred acres of crops and pasture are regularly employed on our comparatively few farms of any size in which intensive agricultural pro- duction is carried on.   This is far above the general average for the whole country on "medium" and large farms.

If our salutary agricultural revolution went so far as to double the manpower associated with "large" farms, an additional 93,000 workers would be needed on such farms. The present ratio is 1·56 persons engaged to 100 acres of *total area* on such farms.   To increase that ratio to 3 would need 93,000 additional workers, as we have just seen.   In fact, if a vigorous attempt were made to establish numerous Economic Farm Centres they would soon run into a man- power bottleneck, except to the extent that surplus family labour would be attracted from smaller farms and per- manently associated with them.   Such a strategic "redeploy- ment" of available agricultural labour would be highly desirable in any case.   More than 200 years ago Bishop Berkeley queried :

"Whether the industry of our people employed in foreign lands, while our own are left uncultivated, be not a great loss to the country?"   And also—

"Whether it would not be much better for us, if, instead of sending our men abroad, we would draw men from the neighbouring countries to cultivate our own?"

These queries are still topical.

The thoughtful reader will have realised that the nucleus of residential workers permanently associated with the Economic Farm Unit would not be just agricultural labourers in the abstract, so to speak.   They would live with and work under the supervision of a competent farm manager who knew all that Glasnevin could teach him about agricul- tural science and had all the other desirable qualifications as well.   Each of his fellow-workers would also be a specialist of some kind, though preferably one who was willing to give a hand wherever it was needed. There would be a specialist for pigs, for cows, for dairying, for poultry, for bees, for horticulture, and for tractors and agricultural machines. There would be abundant, though perhaps not continuous, work for a carpenter, a blacksmith, an electrician, a cabinet-maker, a basket-maker, and men skilled in various other useful crafts. Such craftsmen would reside on the premises and work for the central farm or the immediate neighbourhood as occasion required.

Electric power would be available, for surely such centres would have a high priority in the rural electrification scheme.

With power, skilled management, economic leadership, skilled personnel and surplus labour all available on the spot a rural industrialism, not directly related to agricultural production, would develop by spontaneous generation. For example, motor engineering would be a natural and inevitable outcome of the garage workshop facilities which such a central farm would have to maintain for its own convenience. I can imagine no better foundation for the growth of a very desirable type of rural industrialism.

The workers resident in the mansion would presumably be unmarried—with the exception of the farm manager. In fact, it would be desirable that there should be a "woman of the house" to preside over the domestic amenities and civilise the mere males, as only the right kind of good woman can do. If the farm manager had a wife, and she was prepared to undertake this desirable but arduous rôle, so much the better. But permanent celibacy is not contemplated for the permanent residential workers. As and when they each entered the holy estate they would have to be provided with cottages conveniently near the central premises. In a growing community their places in the big house would be taken by others.

It is desirable that in each case the resident community of co-operative fellow-workers should have, so to speak, a collective soul from the very beginning. Consequently those chosen to constitute such collective entities should have some important common ideals which would constitute a strong emotional bond between them. For example, enthusiasts for the spread of the Irish language might well be chosen to constitute one or more of such collective entities. It ought to be quite easy to find a dozen or a score of such young enthusiasts who also possessed the necessary crafts and skills, and with these at least one experiment could be made and financed by a sympathetic Government. In the course of their daily work, as also in their leisure, such a community would find ample opportunities for modifying their immediate environment in harmony with their Gaelic ideals. Communist cells are a successful method of propaganda organisation for a different kind of ideology. Perhaps the Gaelic League would consider borrowing at least this one idea from that source!

The Gaelic colonies in County Meath have not been an unqualified success from the cultural point of view, and have certainly failed to commend the ideals of Gaelic civilisation to the local residents. At least that is the impression one derives from reading the local papers.

Perhaps this other method would lead to happier results from the point of view of all concerned.

This hour of crisis is also a moment of opportunity and comes as a challenge to us all. It concerns not only indivduals and families, but also groups of persons organised for whatever spiritual or secular purpose. It concerns the priest at the altar and the parson in the pulpit as well as the layman in the pew. But most of all, perhaps, it concerns those voluntary associations of individuals, like Muintir-na-Tire and the Irish Countrywomen's Association, which seek to express a spiritual conception of human society in terms of everyday social and economic relationships, and those other movements, such as the Gaelic League, which strive to influence the quality of the national life and culture as a whole.

In this new Dark Age, when European society is threatened with dissolution and millions of human beings in many countries are struggling to preserve the material conditions of physical survival, all spiritual values are at a heavy discount. And yet there was never a time when it was more important to remember that men—and nations—do not live by bread alone.

It is easier for us to bear this great truth in mind than for other nations which have sunk lower in the scale of human misfortune. Organisations such as those referred to have a special function in associating our spiritual and cultural life with the secular tasks of economic readjustment. Two of them have long been active in this field. But perhaps the Gaelic League can make an even greater contribution, since it is the custodian of a dynamic national ideal as indestructible as the atom. Like the atom, too, its latent energy has tremendous potentialities when harnessed to the social and economic purposes of a peaceful national society.

In the opinion of some the movement to restore a Gaelic civilisation in modern Ireland has hitherto been somewhat parasitic on the national economy. And yet it may well be that it can become an integral and creative element in the growth of a healthier national economy, and a vital force in the building up of a rural civilisation that will warm the hearts of all good Irishmen and exercise a healing influence on a stricken world.

ADDENDUM.

It would be attractive to end this book on this high note. But perhaps a less ambitious approach would be more practical and successful.

After some conversation with General Costello, who is Manager of the Irish Sugar Company, and has a thoroughly realistic outlook on the problems of Irish agriculture, I contributed an article to the "Irish Farmers' Journal," the organ of the Young Farmers' Club Movement in Ireland. In the course of it I suggested that the technique of a Bankers' Cheque Clearing Union might well be applied to Irish agriculture on a local or parochial scale.

I outlined the procedure as follows and attached a specimen of a typical clearing account by way of illustration :—

"*A* is a farmer with 200 statute acres in the townland of   in the parish of   in the county of   . His farm is highly mechanised and he is inclined to specialise in crop cultivation though he also goes in largely for dry cattle, which he buys as stores from a distance. He only keeps three milch cows, but does not rear any of the calves born on his place because his neighbour *D* is a specialist in calf rearing, so he turns them over to *D*. He produces heavy crops of feed potatoes, oats and Ymer barley—more than he can use on his own farm. He sells large quantities of these to *D* and *E*, *D* being a specialist in milk production and *E* in pig breeding. He buys bonhams from *E* and pullets from *F*. He keeps only about 50 hens and does not want the trouble of rearing them. He employs four men regularly about the place, but now that extra labour is no longer casual but organised, he is inclined to expand his beet average, relying on the spare-time labour of certain persons from the households of *D, E, F, G* and *H*. He does a certain amount of cultivating and harvesting for *D, E* and *F*. *A* has a heavy tractor and a light one, but not even *A* can afford to own all the two or three score implements which are necessary for complete mechanisation. It is arranged among them that *C* will acquire a manure spreader and a hay elevator, *D* a Cambridge roller, *E* a potato boiler for silage, etc., etc. He himself has, of course, a corn-drill, a combine harvester, a disc-harrow, a rotovator, a potato spinner, and a threshing mill. The members of the '. . . . Agricultural Clearing Union' get together and arrange a schedule of time rates and/or acreage rates for different kinds of labour and different implements or power units. Produce and livestock would, of course, be exchanged at current local agreed market prices. They also appoint a secretary *X* to keep the records. Thus *A* having done a job with his rotovator for *D* gets *D* to sign a 'chit' like this : 'Debit my a/c for   hours rotovator work.' *A* gives the 'chit' to *X* and down it goes in the a/c—a plus item for *A* and a minus item for *D*. *H* lives in a labourer's cottage and has one acre of garden, which is full of raspberry bushes and apples. He has four sons, one of whom is a skilled horticulturist, who works for the 'Union' as well as in his own garden. Another is a skilled motor mechanic, who has a lorry and a van. *A* is glad to use *H*'s transport equipment from time to time. Every time he uses it he signs a debit note, which *H* deposits with *X*, and, of course, *B, C, D,* and *E, F* and *G* find it useful also.

"*B* is a specialist in milk production, with 20 cows and 30 dry cattle on his 100 acres. He draws on his neighbours heavily for feed, and on balance he owes the clearing a/c at the end of the year.

"*C* has a 200 acre farm, half of it waste land though reclaimable. He has little family labour, so he does little tillage and goes in mostly for dry cattle, feeding them on grass, hay and silage. He buys in stores from his colleagues and at the end of the year his a/c is heavily negative.

"*D*, who has 50 acres, is a specialist in calf rearing. He keeps a Hereford bull and 20 half-Hereford cows, and rears about 60 calves in the year on his cows, buying in the surplus calves. At the end of the year his a/c should be positive.

"E is a specialist in pig breeding. He has 50 acres, and rears about 40 bonhams a year with his four sows. He keeps 6 cows and 18 other cattle and does a certain amount of mixed general farming. His a/c should be nearly neutral.

"F has only 30 acres, so he specialises in raising chickens for sale as pullets and cockerels. He only keeps 3 cows and 12 other cattle and he buys a lot of oats and barley from the 'Union.'

"G, with only 10 acres, specialises in commercial egg production and only keeps a couple of cows.

"We have already noticed that H is practically a land-less man, but his sons have valuable skills, both mechanical and horticultural. One of them does all the pruning and spraying of fruit trees for the neighbours (who formerly neglected their orchards), and they are glad to debit their a/cs with his well-earned reward.

"Below is given, for purposes of illustration only, a specimen of the kind of clearing a/c which would arise as a result of a policy of integrating the farm programmes, machines, implements and skills available on an aggregate of 641 acres. Of course the milk, the large cattle, the wheat, beet, eggs, etc., sold outside the Union membership do not appear in this a/c at all. B's milk cheque should more than pay the £670 he owes the clearing a/c and similarly with regard to G and C.

"Space does not permit a lengthy exposition of the advantages of such an arrangement. Briefly—mechanisation is uneconomic unless there is an adequate number and variety of implements locally available for each power unit locally used. Borrowing and lending as at present practised is unsatisfactory, because people are not so good at returning as at borrowing. A farmer would be more disposed to buy a new implement if he could count on his neighbours helping to pay for it in a regular 'scheduled' way. Tillage will diminish and lazy all-grass farming will return unless we can arrange to aggregate 1,000 acre units for tillage purposes, and the Clearing Union technique will make possible such aggregation *without impairing the individual ownership of his small farm* by the farmer, which in its own way is also a valuable feature of our rural economy."

TABLE XX.

SPECIMEN CLEARING ACCOUNT OF AN A.C.U.

(£'s)

	A	B	C	D	E	F	G	H
Cultivating	+ 100			− 100	− 100			
"	+ 100							
"	+ 50							
Reseeding	+ 250		− 250					
Feed potatoes	+ 20				− 20	− 50		
"	+ 20	− 20						
Feed oats	+ 200	− 200				− 200		
Feed barley	+ 100	− 100						
"	+ 50							
Feed oats	+ 300			− 50	− 50			
Suck calves	+ 50						− 100	
Labour	− 100				+ 100	+ 100		
"	− 100							
Transport	− 200	− 100			+ 100			+ 200
Bonhams	− 100				+ 100			
"								
Yearlings and stores			− 500	+ 500		+ 30		
Pullets			− 30	+ 300		+ 450		
Yearlings and stores			− 300	− 50		− 100	− 200	
Pullets	− 50	− 50	− 50	− 50	− 50		− 100	
Labour and transport		− 200	− 200		− 100			+ 750
	+ 690	− 670	− 1330	+ 550	− 20	+ 230	− 400	+ 950

£ + 2420 } = 0
£ − 2420 }

This map was kindly supplied by Dr. Kenne

A NOTE ON THE BIBLIOGRAPHY

This book is, in the main, based on personal experience, and personal contacts with farmers in different parts of the country, as well as with organisers and officials of co-operative agricultural societies and creameries. Agricultural experts, who were fellow members of various Committees and Commissioners of Inquiry, were also important sources of inspiration and information.

Acknowledgment has been made to some of these persons by name at appropriate places in the text, but most of them have, perforce, no such memorial, though all have deserved it.

Footnotes are an irritating interruption to continuous reading and have been used very sparingly. Where it was obviously desirable to do so, the source of an important piece of information has been given in the actual text.

I attach a list of the most important literary sources consulted, more or less in the order in which they are referred to or used in the text. I hope other students of these matters will find it useful, and that no one will get from it the impression that this is a book written about other books.

J. J.

BIBLIOGRAPHY

LIST OF LITERARY SOURCES CONSULTED.

A. *Government Publications (Irish, unless otherwise stated).*

Reports of the Commission on Agriculture, 1924.

The Agricultural Output of Saorstat Eireann, 1926–27.

The Agricultural Output and the Food Supplies of Great Britain, 1929 (U.K. Report).

Report of the Tariff Commission on Bacon, Hams and other Pig Products, 1932.

Report of the Pig Industries Tribunal, 1933.

Prices Commission Report on the prices charged for Bacon, including hams and gammons, 1938.

Reports of the Commission of Inquiry into Banking, Currency, and Credit, 1938 (commonly known as the Banking Commission Report).

Reports of the Committee of Inquiry on Post-Emergency Agricultural Policy, 1945.

G. A. HOLMES : Report on the present state and methods for improvement of Irish land, 1948.

Agricultural Statistics, 1847–1926.

Agricultural Statistics, 1927–1933.

Statistical Abstracts.

Trade and Shipping Statistics.

Census of Population Reports.

Estimates for Public Services.

Irish Trade Journal.

Ulster Year Books (Northern Ireland Government).

Monthly Reports of Northern Ireland Ministry of Agriculture.

The "History of the Vote": an official document printed for the use of the Resident Commissioner of National Education (last issue 1899).

Recess Committee Report.

B. *General.*

MORITZ J. BONN: Modern Ireland and her Agrarian Problem.

ARTHUR YOUNG: A Tour in Ireland.

Annual Journals of the Statistical and Social Inquiry Society of Ireland.

W. L. MICKS: History of the Congested Districts Board.

MARGARET DIGBY: Horace Plunkett—An Anglo-American Irishman.

HORACE PLUNKETT: Ireland in the New Century.

Agricultural Class Book published by the Commissioners of National Education. Third edition, 1869.

"A Catholic Layman": Mixed Education: The Catholic Case Stated, 1859.

DOREEN WARRINER: Economics of Peasant Farming.

P. LAMARTINE YATES: Food Production in Western Europe.

JOHN BOYD ORR: Food, Health, and Income.

ADAM SMITH: Wealth of Nations.

VISCOUNT ASTOR and B. SEEBOHM ROUNTREE: British Agriculture.

Lewis' Topographical Dictionary.

BISHOP BERKELEY: The Querist.

T. W. FREEMAN: Ireland, its Physical, Historical, Social, and Economic Geography.

JAMES CONNOLLY: Labour in Irish History.

DR. E. E. EVANS: Irish Heritage.

G. HENDERSON: The Farming Ladder.

INDEX

Agricultural Co-operative Movement, 4, 12, 17, 24, 165.

Agricultural Clearing Union, 175 ff.

Agricultural Credit Corporation, 171.

Agricultural, Department of, 20, 22, 26, 29.

Agricultural Output of England and Wales, 1925, 100.

Agricultural Statistics, 1847–1926, 14, 117.

Agricultural Statistics, 1927–1933, 15.

Albert Agricultural College, 26.

Albert Model Farm, 27, 28.

Anderson, R. A., 24.

Artificial Insemination, 111, 152.

Astor and Rountree, *British Agriculture*, 93.

Ballyduff " Centenary " Creamery, 142.

Barbour, Harold, 24.

Barrington, Thomas, " A Review of Irish Agricultural Prices," 37.

Barrow, Major R., 102.

Barton, Robert, on ley farming, 34.

Beddy, Dr., 113, 119.

Beet growing, p. 42.

Berkeley, Bishop, 148, 172.

Better Farming, Better Business, Better Living, 23, 26.

Bonn, Dr. Moritz J., " Modern Ireland and her Agrarian Problem," 3, 5, 6, 8, 9, 10, 11, 12.

Bounties paid by Eire Government, ch. vii, 72 ff.

Bright, John, 5, 7, 8.

Butter production in certain years, 84, 156.

Capital Assets of Irish Agriculture, ch. viii, 87 ff, 119.

Cash crop production and animal husbandry, 32 ff, 42.

" The Catholic Case Stated," 27.

Cattle, ratio of feed costs to, price of, 64.

Cattle, importance of in Irish Economy, 74.

Cereal Equivalent, 43, 45, 48.

College of St. Columba and Agricultural Education, 30.

Commission, Irish Land, 6, 17, 19, 89, 96, 139, 145, 150, 153.

Commission, Banking, 1934–1938, 6, 9, 19, 32, 88, 93 f.

Commission, Pigs, 81.

Commission, Bacon, 81.

Committee of Inquiry on Post-Emergency Agricultural Policy (Majority Report), 14, 16, 34, 44, 110, 157 ; (Terms of Reference), 34.

Communal Organization of Agriculture, 12, ch. xix, 163.

Congested Districts Board, 21.

Connolly, James, 163 f.

Costello, General, 175.

Creameries (co-operative), p. 17, 21, 24, 26.

Creamery-owned farms, 26, ch. xiv, 125, ch. xvi, 139, ch. xvii, 147.

Dairy Products Price " Stabilisation " Acts, 1932–35, 82 ff.

Danish Folk Schools, 167.

Davitt, Michael, 6, 163.

Department of Agriculture, ch. ii, 20 ff., 159.

Department of Statistics, 171.

De Valera, E., 31 ff, 111.

Devoy, John, 6.

Digby, Margaret, biographer of Sir Horace Plunkett, 20, 23.

Dillon, James, 136.

Disestablishment, Irish Church Act, 5, 7.

Donaghmore Creamery, ch. xv, 135 ff.

Dovea Creamery Farm, ch. xvi, 119, 139 ff.

Drinagh Creamery and Farm, 125 ff., 144.

Dual ownership, 11.

Dual purpose cows, 84, 162.

Duncan, G. A., Professor, 32, 41, 94.

Duties, penal levied by British Government, ch. vii, 72 ff.

Economic Farm Units, 166 ff.
Economic War, 3, 31 ff, 41, 46, 49, 55, 57, 63, 65, 69, 84, 110, 154.
Education, Agricultural, 26 ff.
Education, Agricultural, in relation to Secondary, 30.
Education, Agricultural, in relation to Vocational, 29 ff.
Eggs, ratio of, feed costs to, price of, 66.
Exports, Agricultural, 34.
Evans, Dr. E. E., 164 ff.

"Three F's," 6, 7.
Farm and farmyard products, 39 ff.
Farm Improvement Schemes, 157.
Farmyard manure, scarcity of, 33, 57, 77.
Fat cattle, relative decrease in number exported, 75 ff.
Feedstuffs, availability of, 33, 51.
Fertilisers, availability of, 33, 51 ff., 130, 155.
Foot and Mouth disease in 1941, 79.
Freeman, Mr., 161.

Gaelic League, 174 f.
Grass, importance of, 33, 42, 47, 55, 105 ff., 141.
Grass, improvement and mechanisation, 118, 149 ff.
Gurteen Agricultural College, 122 ff.

Hogan, Patrick, 23, 105.
Holdings, number of in different size groups, 14, 159.

Implement Societies, 118 f., 132.
Index of agricultural output, 41, 154, 162.
Integration, local of agricultural effort, 13, ch. xix, 163.
Irish Agricultural Organisation Society, 20, 21.
Irish Countrywomen's Association, 23, 174.
Irish Farmers' Journal, 175.
Irish Trade Journal, 154.

Kanturk's Creamery and Farm, 128 ff., 144.
Kennedy, Dr. Henry, 43, 46, 107, 127.

Lalor, James Fintan, 163.
Land Act of 1903, Wyndham, 3, 9.
Land Act of 1870, 5, 6, 8.
Land Act of 1881, 6, 7, 8, 10.
Land Act of 1887, 7.

Land Act of 1885, Ashbourne, 8, 9.
Land Acts of 1891 and 1896, 8.
Land Act of 1909, 10.
Land Acts of 1923, 10, 19.
Land Act of 1925, 10.
Land Act of 1933, 19.
Land Purchase, 7, 8, 9, 10.
Land Reclamation Scheme, 157f.
Leasehold, 5, 7.
Ley farming, 34, 43, 157.
Limerick County, types of cattle in, in certain years, 85.
Livestock Breeding Act, 1925, 109.
Live Stock (Artificial Insemination) Act, 111.
Livestock and livestock products, proportion of in agricultural output, 37.
Livestock, importance of in Irish agriculture, 42, 44, 55, 107.
Livestock policy, ch. x, 109 ff.
Livestock, numbers of, 58 ff, 66, 70, 156.

McKinney, Rev. J. W., 123.
Marshall Aid, 157.
Materials (raw) for Irish Animal Husbandry, ch. iv, 35 ff.
Mechanisation, progress of, ch. xii, 116 ff., 159 ff.
Micks, W. L., 21.
Milford Creamery and Farm, 131 ff., 144.
Milk price subsidy, 26, 110, 162.
Ministry of Food as buyer of Irish fat cattle, 75 ff.
Mitchelstown Creamery, 107, 111, 129, 144, ch. xvii, 147, 166, 170.
Model Agricultural Schools, 27 ff.
Muintir-na-Tire, 4, 174.
Murphy, Mr., paper read to Statistical Society, 92, 93, 95, 98.

National Board of Education, 27, 29.
New Zealand, additional payment to, 78.
Northern Ireland, comparisons with, 154 f.
Northern Ireland agricultural situation after 1922, 31.
Northern Ireland, pig production in, 68.

Oatcrop, proportion of, fed to livestock, 41, 44.
O'Grady, Standish, 24.
Orpen, Senator Richard, 166 f.

Parnell, Charles Stewart, 6, 22.
Pasture, area of, 42.
Patterson scheme, 82.
Physical volume of Agricultural Production, 41.
Pigs, 58, 68 f., 149.
Ploughed land, area of, 42, 117.
Plunkett, Sir Horace, 4, 20, 21, 24, 26.
Policy, Agricultural, agencies of, ch. ii, 20 ff.
Policy, Agricultural, after 1922, ch. iii, 31 ff.
Poultry Hatcheries Act, 115.
Poultry, 65 f.
Poultry policy, ch. xi, 112 ff.
Poultry Statistics, 66, 112.
Poultry, incubation, 114, 126, 132.
" Population," cows, pigs, etc., 58 ff.
Prices, fall of agricultural, 6.
Prices, feed costs and animal product prices, ch. vi, 56 ff.
Prices, differential, 57, 77, 85, 126.
Prices, of milk at creameries, 85.
Price ratios, importance of, ch. v, 49 ff., ch. vi, 56 ff., 115.
Protein Equivalent, 43.

Recess Committee, 22, 27 ff.
Roche, Mr., 149.
Rural Domestic Economy Schools, 121.
Rural Electrification Scheme, 126 f., 132, 137, 173.
Russell George (AE), 24.
Russell, T. W., 22, 23.

Security of tenure, 6, 7, 9.
Self-sufficiency, importance of grass for, 47.

Silage, 107, 127, 140, 151, 159.
Smith, Adam, on importance of cattle in agricultural improvement, 56.
Starch Equivalent, 43.
Statistical Abstract, 10, 15, 92.
Statistical and Social Inquiry Society of Ireland, 13, 88, 102, 113, 119, 166.
Store cattle, relative increase in number exported, 75 f.
Subletting, 10.
Subsidy to I.A.O.S., 23.
Subsidies (and bounties), 84, 110.

Tillage products, importance of, in animal husbandry, 46 ff., 55.
Trant, Captain, 139 ff.

Ulster Custom, 5, 7.
Ulster Year Book, 10.
United Kingdom, Agricultural Price Policies, 31, 33.

Johnstone-Wallace, D. B., in The Farmers' Weekly, 18.
Wheat acreage in Economic War and second World War, 41 f., 55.
Women on the farm, ch. xiii, 120 ff.
World Wars, effect on Irish Agriculture, 31 ff., 41, 47, 68, 117, 129, 154 ff.

Yearly tenancies, 5.
Young, Arthur, 4.
Young Farmers' Clubs, 4, 13, 26, 175.